BEYOND BRUNDTLAND

Green Development in the 1990s

THIJS DE LA COURT

Translated by Ed Bayens and Nigel Harle

New Horizons Press
New York

Zed Books Ltd
London and New Jersey

Beyond Brundtland: Green Development in the 1990s
was first published in English in 1990 by:

Zed Books Ltd.
57 Caledonian Road
London N1 9BU, UK
and
171 First Avenue
Atlantic Highlands
New Jersey 07716, USA

First paperback edition published in the United States of
America by:

New Horizons Press, an imprint of
Council on International and Public Affairs
777 United Nations Plaza
New York, NY 10017

Cover designed by Sophie Buchet.
Typeset by EMS Photosetters, Rochford, Essex.
Printed and bound in the United Kingdom by
Biddles Ltd, Guildford and Kings Lynn.

British Library Cataloguing in Publication Data

Court, Thijs de la
  Beyond Brundtland : green development in the 1990's.
  1. Economic development. Environmental aspects.
  I. Title. II. Onze gezamenlijke toekomst, het brundtland –
    rapport kritisch bekeken. *English.*
  330.9

  ISBN 0-86232-904-3
  ISBN 0-86232-905-1 pbk

Library of Congress Cataloging-in-Publication Data

Court, Thijs de la.
    (Onze gezamenlijke toekomst. English)
    Beyond Brundtland : green development in the 1990s/
Thijs de la Court : translated by Ed Bayens and Nigel Harle.
    p.   cm.
    Translation of: Onze gezamenlijke toekomst.
    ISBN 0-945257-27-9 (New Horizons Press) : $11.50.
    1. Economic development – Environmental aspects. 2.
Economic development – Environmental aspects – Developing
countries.
    I. Title.
HD75.6.C89513   1990
363.7–dc20

Beyond Brundtland was originally published in 1988
  in Dutch as *Onze Gezamenlijke Toekomst: Milieu,
  ontwapening – Het Brundtland-rapport kritisch bekeken*
  by BijEEN, 's Hertogenbosch, The Netherlands.

Contents

Foreword

When the United Nations' World Commission on Environment and Development (WCED) published its report in 1987, thousands of agendas were drawn up and appointments made. The Report, entitled *Our Common Future*, tabled a problem in need of urgent discussion. More and more people are becoming aware that development, disarmament and environmental protection are inter-related issues. In the Report concrete facts were presented: no abstract discourses, but first-hand experiences and hard data that made it painfully clear that something must be done — now.

This critical resumé of the Brundtland Report, named after Gro Harlem Brundtland, Prime Minister of Norway, who chaired the Commission, was first published in the Netherlands. Following publication of the WCED Report, Dutch environment, peace and Third World groups, combined in the Alliance for Sustainable Development, reacted with a joint report of their own. To make the findings of this report accessible to interested lay people, the Alliance, a non-governmental organization, also commissioned a summary of the original 380 pages, with comments where called for. The result is presented here, in English translation. Much of the text comes straight from the Brundtland Report. Direct quotations from the Report or from its official summary are clearly indicated as such. Where commentary is given, this is explicitly mentioned.

It is worth adding that the commentary is critical, coming from people with a long experience of working on environmental, development and peace issues. The Brundtland Report contains much useful information and offers a good starting point for discussion. But in many cases its conclusions are not shared by environmental, peace and Third World organizations. For the hope offered us by the Commission assumes continued rapid economic growth plus a modernization of production processes. Of course, clean and efficient technologies are needed on a large scale, but as a solution they do not touch upon the real core of the crisis with which we are confronted. Instead, what we need are a just sharing of power, access to natural resources on the part of local populations, and the conservation of the cultural and social integrity of the different societies of the world. These are the keys to a future which is really 'sustainable'. Development must grow from within, and should not be imposed from the outside.

Thijs de la Court
World Information Service on Environment and Development
1990

1. Towards Sustainable Development

What is currently at stake is the conservation of the Earth and the biosphere, the thin layer that is the scene of all of life. Desertification, deforestation, erosion, ozone depletion, acid rain and the greenhouse effect are just a few of the threats facing us. Another spectre is that of nuclear war, which would certainly be the end of everything. Human suffering and the destruction of Nature are everyday realities. At the same time, the call for action is becoming louder. Something must be done before Man effectively destroys the world; this awareness is gaining ground at all levels. Can there be anyone who has not seen the pictures of starving Africa? And who does not remember the nuclear disaster at Chernobyl in the Soviet Union? The question is: how can we turn the tide, how can we create and preserve a future for coming generations, with adequate scope for Nature and a healthy environment?

Our Common Future

In 1983 the General Assembly of the United Nations set up the World Commission on Environment and Development (WCED). Chaired by the present Prime Minister of Norway, Dr. Gro Harlem Brundtland, the Commission was formed by representatives from 21 countries in all regions of the world. For three years this group of scientists, senior civil servants and politicians, more than half of whom were from the developing countries, studied and discussed peace, development and environmental issues. A long series of studies was produced, and public hearings were held on five continents. In April 1987 the results were published in the form of a book entitled *Our Common Future*. In the autumn of the same year the Brundtland Commission, as it is informally known, presented its report to the 42nd session of the General Assembly of the United Nations.

9

Agenda for Change

The main task of the Brundtland Commission was to prepare a global agenda for change. To this end, three objectives were formulated:

- To study the critical environmental and development problems and formulate realistic proposals for addressing them;

- To suggest new forms of international co-operation intended to promote the changes needed to solve these problems;

- To raise the awareness of individuals, activists, organizations, business enterprises, institutes and governments and increase their readiness to take action.

History of the Report

In its general content and scope, the Brundtland Report is in the tradition of such publications as *The Limits to Growth* by the Club of Rome (1972), *The Brandt Report* published under the chairmanship of Willy Brandt (1980) and *Global 2000*, prepared for the then US President Jimmy Carter (1981). The first of these, especially, had a major impact on world opinion when it appeared in the early seventies. Its core message was that the enormous global economic expansion initiated after the Second World War could not continue for ever. The world would run out of natural resources, and the environment become poisoned. It was at this time that the United Nations organized the first major conference on the environment, in Stockholm in 1972.

What Makes It Different

There are two aspects that distinguish the Brundtland Report from the other studies. In the first place, the Brundtland Commission points out the strong link between poverty and environmental problems. The Report states that:

> Today's environmental challenges arise both from the lack of development and from the unintended consequences of some forms of economic growth. Many forms of development erode the environmental resources upon

Western consumerism has penetrated the rice paddies of the Philippines.
(Wolf Krabel)

which they must be based, and environmental degradation can undermine economic development. Poverty is a major cause and effect of global environmental problems. It is therefore futile to attempt to deal with environmental problems without a broader perspective that encompasses the factors underlying world poverty and international inequality.

In the second place, the Brundtland Commission, unlike the Club of Rome, is optimistic. The summary of the Brundtland Report states:

> Our Report is not a prediction of ever increasing environmental decay, poverty, and hardship in an ever more polluted world among ever decreasing resources. We see instead the possibility for a new era of economic growth, one that must be based on policies that sustain and expand the environmental resource base. And we believe such growth to be absolutely essential to relieve the great poverty that is deepening in much of the developing world.

Some of the Threats

- **Desertification:** each year six million hectares (60,000 square kilometres) of fertile soil are being transformed into worthless desert.

- **Deforestation:** each year hundreds of thousands of square kilometres of tropical forest are being destroyed or seriously degraded (in 1988 more than 200,000 sq. km. in Amazonia alone). Part of the land is used for agriculture but the soil quality is such that yields are low, certainly in the long run.

- **Acid Rain:** the acidification of rain is killing forests and lakes, destroying our cultural heritage in the form of buildings and statues, and causing irreparable damage to the soil.

- **The Greenhouse Effect**, in part caused by the burning of coal, oil and gas, in part by wholesale destruction of forests and other vegetation, will early next century bring about shifts in areas with a viable agriculture, wreak havoc with the world's

➜

⇨ natural ecosystems, cause sea levels to rise and
disrupt weather patterns.

- **The Depletion of the Ozone Layer** will cause a
major increase in the incidence of skin cancer in
humans and animals and seriously disrupt the food
chains of the oceans.

- **Toxic Substances** from industrial and
agricultural activities are entering food chains and
penetrating underground water supplies, posing an
untold threat to public health and ecological
integrity.

- **The Extinction of Animal and Plant Species**
and the resultant loss of genetic diversity is
robbing present and future generations of
resources for use in agriculture, medicine and
industry.

Based on a survey by W. C. Rey, Director-General of the Dutch
Ministry for Housing, Regional Development and the Environ-
ment, from *Environment and Development: Proceedings*, IVM,
Amsterdam, 1987. ■

Criticisms of Brundtland

The Brundtland Report has stirred up many reactions. Environmental,
peace and Third World organizations, business corporations, banks,
governments and parliaments have reacted in many different ways,
though with a common undertone that recognizes the importance of
the discussion started. And in that respect the Brundtland Report,
almost all are agreed, certainly has its merits. Likewise, the body of
data contained in the Report, and thus presented to policy makers, is
widely appreciated.

Criticism by environmental, Third World and peace organizations
is directed mainly at the form of development advocated by the
Commission. Anupam Mishra, an Indian environmentalist, stated
that: 'The Report has been unable to avoid the contradictions inherent
in the concept of "development". It has followed all governments and
UN documents in highlighting poverty and the population explosion

Women of the Appiko (Chipko) movement, Karnataka, South India.
February 1989. (R. Berriedale – Johnson/Panos Pictures)

as the biggest obstacles to environmental conservation.' Anupam Mishra refers to the words of Mahatma Gandhi, the great advocate of an independent, free India. When asked by a British colonial whether he hoped to approximate Britain's standard of living after India achieved independence, he replied: 'It took Britain half the resources of the planet to achieve this prosperity; how many planets will a country like India require?'

People using this Western scale of 'standard of living' fail to understand, Anupam Mishra argues, that the real cause of environmental destruction, increasing poverty and a growing world population lies in their own prescription of a Western standard of living for everybody, and not vice versa. But all governments today — whether they be democracies, military dictatorships or religious fundamentalist regimes — are united in their efforts to achieve a Western standard of living for their people. And in this process they are ready to sell their nation's soil, water, forests, minerals, air, and even women and children to the merchants and moneylenders of the West. If bringing Western development was so necessary, our governments could have encouraged, he says, a healthy debate on the question, convincing the people of its importance for their own well-being. But they chose the other way — of ridiculing us, by labelling our culture as backward, by branding our simple knowledge as ignorance and superstition and then forcing us to join their elitist race for scientific development to make us 'civilized'.

Together with many other individuals and organizations, Anupam Mishra is angered by the Brundtland Report's definition of development — and this is indeed an important criticism, for the Brundtland Commission's own analysis is based on a certain conception of development, and thus of economic growth.

The Chipko Movement

Five o'clock in the morning. It is dark and cold at the bus station of Rishikesh, a place of pilgrimage at the foot of the Himalayas. Here the Ganges is a cool mountain stream, still oblivious of the meandering course it is to follow across the plains of India. White summits, breath-taking gorges. The land is barren, the roads continually blocked by avalanches of rocks from the mountains. A jolting bus, performing the duties of a ➡

⇨

Landrover, picks its way through rocks, pot-holes and oncoming traffic, its shrill hooter resounding among the mountains. After travelling for hours, I get out in Tehri Garhwal. Up to my ankles in mud, I see the pale sun just rising above the houses, imparting a drab colour to the market street. With a population of 15,000, Tehri is a focus of economic activity, with bus links far into the Himalayan snows. It is one of the centres of the Chipko movement, a movement that has gained fame and respect for the courage of its women — for the majority of the activists are women — in embracing trees to save them from the axe. Tehri Garhwal has always been a hotbed of resistance. In the 19th century already, the inhabitants of this small Himalayan town saw how their British rulers were destroying their forests. Their popular resistance was not able to stop the destruction, however. In 1930 they started a movement of non-cooperation. The fight for the forests grew fiercer. Blockades were violently pulled down; many villagers were killed or injured. On September 10, 1942, one of the leaders of the movement, Saklani, raised the flag of the Indian Congress Party in the town square. He was immediately arrested, together with many others, and imprisoned in a dank cellar for a year. He was severely tortured, but when released, physically broken, he resumed the fight for the forest. It was this man Saklani, now old, but still active, whom I went to visit in Tehri.

I found him deeply engrossed in his books. A gentle man, a lawyer and for a long time mayor of Tehri. Sweet tea in the wintry sun, with a panorama of eroded mountains. 'It has not always been like this,' says Saklani. 'The mountains were green and this valley yielded enough food for all of us. There was no hunger. We could get enough from the forests and from our fields, which were laid out between carefully constructed ridges stretching high up the mountain slopes.' Saklani points towards the stony faces of the mountains. 'After the British, and later the kings, had taken away the timber, things went badly for us. Where could we find the things we needed? The climate changed. Winters

➡

⇨

became cold. The rivers filled up with stones, and now each spring there are floods. There are no longer any trees to hold the soil. There is no soil to absorb the water.'

Saklani is the leader of a movement that is opposing the construction of the highest dam to be built in the whole of Asia. With a motion of his chin, he indicates the place where the bare mountains form a narrow gorge and the river roars down southward, before changing into the slow-moving Ganges that meanders across the plains. 'We are against this dam, because it will destroy our land, our houses, our history. But the most shocking thing about this project is that the dam is to be built on a geological fault. Earthquakes are common here. And yet on this very spot they choose to build a dam 260 metres high. If it breaks, a wall of water more than 70 metres high will force its way through the mountains! No one will survive such an event. And once it has reached the plains of the Ganges, the flood will fan out over a wide area. The 3.5 billion cubic metres of water will burst out of the reservoir, causing the Ganges to overflow all the way down to Calcutta. It is sheer murder,' says Saklani.

A once prosperous land is fated to disappear under water. Is this progress?

The little town has meanwhile come alive. Cows eat cardboard and paper and stroll leisurely through the narrow streets. Schoolchildren and students accompany me, practising their English: 'How are you, mister?' The sun is radiant. Tehri is a cheerful, colourful town, and it is hard to realize that in a few years' time it will be submerged under many metres of water. Past the bus station, walking along the river, I see the remnants of a bridge (swept away by floods caused by deforestation . . .) and reach the dam construction site. The muddy road winds upward, past the corrugated iron barracks of the labourers, who need to be recruited in far-off regions. There are no local people working on the dam, as this would make the project vulnerable to sabotage. The working conditions are horrible; many

➡

⇨

labourers have died on the job. At the top I meet the
chief engineer, Dr. Y. P. Singh. A nice man. 'We will be
anchoring the mountain sides that threaten to collapse,'
he explains in a fatherly way. 'There are just a few
vulnerable places.' A glance around us, up the steep,
eroded slopes, where avalanches are frequent, leaves
quite a different impression. 'We're not afraid of
earthquakes. The dam will hold, and after all, we do
need energy. India must modernize. We'll be doing all
we can to minimize the risks, but you must remember,
an energy shortage is also dangerous.'

After nightfall we talk in a small group — by candlelight,
for there is a power failure. The conversation keeps
drifting back to the dam, destroyer of all perspectives.
'We have everything here,' says one of the Chipko
people. 'We have schools, farms, our own power supply,
small businesses. For this, we have had to fight hard.
How many times did we block the road? How many
meetings did we organize? How many trips did we make
to all the villages here to convince the people of the
potential of this land? First the British felled our trees,
then the Indian oppressors. And now they are going to
flood it all.'

But the fighting spirit is still very much in evidence.
Saklani, the last in a line of four generations of lawyers:
'The constitution prohibits any activities endangering
human life. We have crates full of evidence, and our case
has been accepted by the High Court. If the judge
considers the case objectively, he will prohibit
construction of the dam, in spite of the amount of
money involved.'

It is late when we say farewell. I've been told about
weaving mills, biogas, schools, women's projects,
reforestation, cattle breeding and scores of other
activities developed by the local people. 'If only we get a
chance, without the outside world determining what is
going to happen to us. For we must live here, and so we
are the ones who must choose how we live.' It was still
dark when the shrill hooter of the bus announced the
journey back.

■

2. Common Concerns

The key concept of the Brundtland Report is **sustainable development**, defined as 'development that meets the needs of the present without compromising the ability of future generations to meet their own needs.'

> Many present efforts to guard and maintain human progress, to meet human needs, and to realize human ambitions are simply unsustainable — in both the rich and poor nations. They draw too heavily, too quickly, on already overdrawn environmental resource accounts to be affordable far into the future. They may show profits on the balance sheets of our generation, but our children will inherit the losses.

> We borrow environmental capital from future generations with no intention or prospect of repaying. They may damn us for our spendthrift ways, but they can never collect on our debt to them. We act as we do because we can get away with it: future generations do not vote; they have no political or financial power; they cannot challenge our decisions.

Underdevelopment

The Brundtland Report shows that the international economic dependence of countries is decisive for the environment. **An International Sustainable Economic Order** is called for:

> Developing countries face the dilemma of having to use commodities as exports, in order to break foreign exchange constraints on growth, while also having to minimize damage to the environmental resource base supporting this growth. The prices of their commodity exports do not fully reflect the environmental costs to the resource base. Their dependence on the world market, which also determines the prices of their export products, forces developing countries to bear the hidden costs of increasing overuse of the natural resource base themselves. Obsolete production

19

The camel: more than a means of transport for nomadic peoples. Mauritania. (Klijn/Present)

processes often take a heavy environmental toll. In 1980 the industries of developing countries exporting to Organization for Economic Co-operation and Development (OECD) members would have incurred direct pollution control costs of $5.5 billion if they had been required to meet the environmental standards then prevailing in the United States.

So states the Brundtland Commission. Indirect costs, arising from such problems as erosion through deforestation, climatic change and an increasing incidence of new diseases, represent many times this sum.

Africa as an Example

Many Third World countries are in an economic fix. On the one hand, the prices of their exports — raw materials, such as ores and minerals, or agricultural products, such as cotton, sugar or coffee — are decreasing, while on the other, loan redemption and interest payments are exerting ever greater pressure. This results in further environmental degradation, for Third World countries are thus forced to exploit the limited capital tied up in their natural resources. Brundtland puts it very clearly:

> The recent crisis in Africa best and most tragically illustrates the ways in which economics and ecology can interact destructively and trip into disaster. Triggered by drought, its real causes lie deeper. They are to be found, in part, in national policies that gave too little attention, too late, to the needs of smallholder agriculture and to the threats posed by rapidly rising populations. Their roots extend also to a global economic system that takes more out of a poor continent than it puts in. Debts that they cannot pay force African nations relying on commodity sales to overuse their fragile soils, thus turning good land into desert.

> Trade barriers in the wealthy nations — and in many developing ones — make it hard for Africans to sell their goods for reasonable returns, putting yet more pressure on ecological systems.

In the autumn of 1987 the United Nations published an alarming report on the economic dependence of Africa. Its main conclusions were:

- Debt repayments increased on average to more than half the income from exports. In some cases, more than 100 per cent of export income was spent on debt servicing, leaving nothing for the elementary necessities of life.

- The seventeen poorest African countries must pay almost $7 billion in debts in 1988–90, which is more than three times the sum they paid in 1985.

- In 1986 Africa had to spend $15 billion on debt repayments.

- In the same year Africa lost $19 billion because prices of its export products dropped.

- Total transfer of resources to Africa decreased to $18 billion in 1986, mainly because of the decrease in development aid.

- Export credits dropped from $1 billion in 1985 to $0.4 billion in 1986. In 1987 hardly any credits were granted.

- Other private loans decreased from $3.5 billion in 1985 to $1.5 billion in 1986.

- Africa's total debt is approaching the $200 billion mark. This equals half the continent's overall GNP and three to four times its annual income from exports.

Africa: Resource Flows

Into Africa, 1986

Income, in dollars, from:
(i) development aid	16 billion
(ii) private loans	2 billion
Total	18 billion

Out of Africa, 1986

Losses, in dollars, from:
(i) export price falls	19 billion
(ii) loan redemption obligations	15 billion
Total	34 billion

At the end of 1986, Africa consequently was $16 billion poorer.

Sources: UN Economic Commission for Africa and Organization for Economic Co-operation and Development.

Economic Growth

To the Brundtland Commission, the fight against poverty forms the main thrust of the answer to environmental problems. In their view, economic growth is the remedy for poverty:

> Poverty is not only an evil in itself, but sustainable development requires meeting the basic needs of all and extending to all the opportunity to fulfil their aspirations for a better life. A world in which poverty is endemic will always be prone to ecological and other catastrophes. Meeting essential needs requires not only a new era of economic growth for nations in which the majority are poor, but an assurance that those poor get their fair share of the resources required to sustain that growth.

Cause and Effect

Is environmental destruction the cause of poverty or its effect? This is a crucial question, for it has wide-reaching implications for the choice of strategy to be adopted. According to the Brundtland Commission: 'Today's environmental challenges arise both from the lack of development and from the unintended consequences of some forms of economic growth.' Although it issues a very clear warning against the hazards of further industrialization, it concludes that we must industrialize (a five- to tenfold increase in global industrial output is envisaged) if poverty is to be overcome. In doing so, optimum use should be made of clean technologies. But is poverty really the cause? An example will show that this is often not the case.

Deforestation

In a subsequent chapter deforestation will be discussed at length; here, a summary illustration is presented.

In Senegal traditional, small-scale forms of agriculture have always been practised. Famines were rare thanks to proper land distribution, and when drought threatened their herds the herdsmen moved to wetter areas.

This situation continued unchanged until the introduction of money and frontiers, which gave Senegal a place in the world economy. As the land proved to be very suitable for peanut cultivation, thousands of hectares of the best land were used to grow peanuts for the export market. Major investments were required for irrigation

Public transport in Afghanistan. (Wolf Krabel)

facilities and transport to the ports. Foreign capital, in the form of loans and grants, provided the solution.

How did this 'development' affect local farmers, and especially the women? They and their families lost their best land. The valleys were deforested and used for export crops, while farming families still growing food had to move to the hills, where no good land was to be found. They took possession of meagre plots. Some of them received government grants to buy a plot, others had to spend their savings, but many of them moved in illegally. The land was so poor that in a few years it was virtually exhausted. Thousands of families grew poorer and poorer. The soil was rapidly washed away, causing massive erosion of the hillsides. The rain created deep gullies in the mountain slopes. The rivers became brown with the soil they carried away. In short, an environmental disaster.

Is poverty to blame for this? In this case, and the same holds for most of the environmental disasters in the Third World, the cause was exploitation of man and the soil for exports to the Western world.

Growth: The Answer?

Economic growth is not a simple concept. In most cases it stands for growth of the Gross National Product. Is the answer to be found in higher production, as advocated by the Brundtland Commission? Many organizations have their doubts. In their view, it is precisely this economic growth that causes environmental destruction. To them, sustainable development means that natural resources are used in such a way as to enable us to live in harmony with the environment and with each other until far into the future. For this, it is essential that groups of people, in whatever part of the world, can determine their own development. The diversity of cultures on earth is the result of many centuries in which people have adapted themselves to the environment surrounding them, and this adaptation process proves to be the best guarantee for sustainable development. Since the colonial era, however, the adaptation process has been widely and thoroughly disrupted.

Cultural Diversity

Anil Agarwal, board member of one of the largest international environmental organizations, the Environmental Liaison Centre,

Nairobi, voices the essence of the criticism of the Brundtland Report in an appeal to the 'Western world': 'What can you do? First, I think that if you want to live in a world with a healthy environment you should learn to respect cultural diversity. The cultural diversity of the world of two hundred years ago, before we created this multinational culture that is more dangerous than a multinational enterprise, has gone. It was a direct result of biological diversity. People in different parts of the world had found different ways of doing things. It is an astounding fact that today there is actually less discipline as regards land use than there was two hundred years ago, when population pressure was lower. In every village of 18th century India the use of natural resources was controlled. The village headman decided how shifting agriculture should be carried out and who could use the land. Rediscovering one's own traditional culture is a surprising experience. And this is true not only for India. You discover the same things in Africa and in so many other cultures of the world that have now been destroyed. That is why we will have to develop a very profound respect for other cultures if we want to live in a sustainable world. Today, the dominant cultures of the world have the power to destroy the other cultures. If this happens, we will have no peace and no sustainable growth.'

Cars

Imagine a world practically without cars. Only the buses, a few lorries, ambulances, fire engines and other specialist vehicles. The environment would be all the better for it. Cars are responsible for almost half the air pollution in industrialized countries. In addition, oil refineries, service stations, car spraying shops, tyre factories and road construction all serve cars and damage the environment.

At only a fraction of the cost of cars, excellent public transport could be provided. Local economies would be strengthened, for the shop or factory around the corner is the easiest to reach. Employment would be boosted, too, for local small-scale companies are labour-intensive.

Dependence on raw materials would diminish. For cars, chromium and platinum are needed. The greater part of

⇨ world chromium output is used in the automobile industry. Chromium and platinum are also mainstays of the South African economy. By reducing car traffic, we help fight apartheid!

Current traffic intensity in the countries of Northwest Europe would be simply impossible on a world scale because of the prohibitive energy and raw material requirements.

The Third World

In developing countries, too, car use is rapidly increasing. As in so many of the industrialized countries, the road system cannot cope with the intensity of traffic, raw materials are consumed, foreign dependence increases, and environmental pollution is further aggravated. In North Africa, trucks and jeeps are ousting camels. Cars give speed, power, status. Camels offer food, milk, dung, transport, shadow in the daytime and warmth at night. Camels are more reliable and cheaper, are part of the culture of the desert people, and are eminently adapted to local conditions.

3. The Challenges

Although the number of problems facing the world seems infinite, some central themes can be lifted out of the Report.

In many people's view, the enormous growth of world population — the five billion mark was passed in 1987 — will inevitably lead to problems. We do not have enough food or other resources to feed the Earth's anticipated eight to twelve billion inhabitants in the next century. Though this is disputable, there are many who think that population growth and food supplies constitute the central problems of our time. More and more nature reserves are falling victim to bulldozers, motorways or chain saws. Each year 7.5 to 10 million hectares of tropical forest are destroyed — an area the size of Austria. An equal area is seriously degraded each year.

The list of major threats sadly does not end here. Our energy supplies are limited. The recent international conflict in the Persian Gulf may only be a prelude to the problems that might arise if oil really becomes scarce. Another problem perhaps far more serious in scope and implications is the fuelwood crisis. Each day millions of women walk long distances carrying heavy loads of fuelwood. Often they cannot find enough to cook their food. And the time spent looking for fuelwood cannot be used for agricultural activities.

There are two other major problem areas. Increasing industrialization is having an enormous impact on the environment. Chemical wastes, land scarcity and air pollution are only a few of the problems it creates. In addition, growing urbanization is a problem that is threatening to move completely beyond our control. In 1940 one out of every hundred people were living in cities larger than a million inhabitants, while in 1980 this had increased to one in ten. This represents a gigantic shift, and metropolises like Mexico City, Bombay, Calcutta or Sao Paulo now form ominous symbols of what the future may hold.

What about Health?

Region	Life expectancy (years)		Child mortality (deaths per 1000 children)	
	1950–55	1980–88	1960–65	1980–85
World	49.9	64.6	117	81
Africa	37.5	49.7	157	114
Asia	41.2	57.9	133	87
South America	52.3	64.0	101	64
North America	64.4	71.1	43	27
Europe	65.3	73.2	37	16
Soviet Union	61.7	70.9	32	25
Oceania	61.0	67.6	35	39

Source: WCED, based on data from the World Resources Institute/International Institute for Environment and Development, *World Resources, 1986* (New York: Basic Books, 1986).

(1) Population and Natural Resources

Since the summer of 1987 the Earth has been supporting more than five billion people, and the number is still growing. According to the United Nations this population growth will stabilize in the course of the next century. Forecasters hope that by 2010 most people will have at most two children, in which case there will be a population of 7.7 billion by 2060. However, if the maximum of two children per couple is not reached until 2065, for instance, the world population will stabilize at 14.2 billion people in the year 2100. Optimistically, the Brundtland Commission takes these figures to show that sound demographic policies can exert considerable influence on population pressure.

Present rates of population growth cannot continue. They already compromise many governments' abilities to provide education, health care, and food security for people, much less their abilities to raise living standards. The gap between numbers and resources is all the more compelling because so much of the population growth is concentrated in low-income countries, ecologically disadvantaged countries, and poor households. Yet the population issue is not solely about numbers. And poverty and resource degradation can exist on thinly populated lands, such as the drylands and the tropical forests.

The Brundtland Commission warns against attributing all environmental problems to the population problem. 'Threats to the sustainable use of resources come as much from inequalities in people's access to resources and from the ways in which they use them.' An inhabitant of an industrialized country consumes far more and causes far greater pressure on natural resources than an inhabitant of a Third World country. The developed countries, with one quarter of the world's population, consume about 80 per cent of commercial energy and metals, 85 per cent of all paper, and more than half of the fat contained in food.

Still, most people consider population growth to be a central problem. And not without reason. Developing countries in Africa, Asia and Latin America are witnessing a rapid population growth. According to the Commission the matter is a complex one, however.

In most cases, birth and death rates have dropped:

- Thirty-two per cent of the people in the Third World live in countries, such as China and the Republic of Korea, with birth rates below 25 (per 1000 population, per year) and death rates below 10.

- Forty-one per cent are in countries where birth rates have fallen, but not as much as death rates, and their populations are growing at around 2 per cent — doubling, in other words, every 34 years. Such countries include Brazil, India, Indonesia, and Mexico.

- The remaining 27 per cent live in countries, such as Algeria, Bangladesh, Iran, and Nigeria, where death rates have fallen slightly but birth rates remain high. Overall population growth is in the range of 2.5 to 3 per cent (doubling every 23 to 28 years), with even higher growth rates in some countries, such as Kenya (4.4 per cent).

Problems

What are the problems created by this population explosion? According to the Brundtland Commission, the greatest problems will concern food supplies. It cites a study by the United Nations Food and Agriculture Organization (FAO) which gives calculations of the amount of food the Earth can produce. The study concludes that, without introduction of any new technologies, by the year 2000 there will still be 117 countries capable of producing enough food for one and a half times their expected populations.

By implication, there will be several countries whose outlook is less bright. Sixty-four countries, with 1.1 billion people, will not be able to satisfy their own food requirements. In these countries, population growth is so high, and the available land surface so small, that they will need to import food. Most of these are high-income countries such as Taiwan, the Philippines and Singapore. They have enough money to import food, but this presupposes surplus food production elsewhere. The UN study concludes that investments in agricultural modernization are called for if the increasing demand is to be met. This issue will be dealt with in greater detail below, in the section on food.

Measures to be Taken

It is always very difficult to propose measures on a global scale. There are countries, such as China, where the population issue now commands a prominent place in government policy. Some countries, such as Malaysia and France, would like their population to grow. Political, cultural and religious differences make it difficult to formulate a single unifying proposal. Nevertheless, there is scope for developing demographic policies that are generally acceptable. In the first place, there must be optimum safeguards for the economic position of the people. Poverty stimulates population growth:

> Families poor in income, employment, and social security need children first to work and later to sustain elderly parents. Measures to provide an adequate livelihood for poor households, to establish and enforce minimum-age child labour laws, and to provide publicly financed social security will all lower fertility rates. Improved public health and child nutrition programmes — so parents do not need 'extra' children as insurance against child death — can also help to reduce fertility levels. All these programmes are effective in bringing down birth rates only when their benefits are shared by the majority.

A society with high economic growth from which the poor do not benefit is characterized by a higher birth rate.

Besides these social and economic checks, the Brundtland Commission also mentions the role of women:

> Fertility rates fall as women's employment opportunities outside the home and farm, their access to education, and their age at marriage all rise. Hence policies meant to lower fertility rates not only must include economic incentives and disincentives, but must aim to improve the position of

women in society. Such policies should essentially promote women's rights.

Halting Population Growth: The Top Priority?

Should halting population growth be given top priority? The Brundtland Report does not answer this question, but its members and advisors did indicate how important they consider the issue. One of them is Dr. Vincent Cable, a member of the British parliament and advisor to the Brundtland Commission:

> In many cases the major priority is to slow population growth. Where population is growing at over 3 per cent, it is difficult to see how a disastrous cycle of declining living standards and a deteriorating environment can be averted. There is no short cut to lower birth rates. Until poor families see that family planning will bring higher living standards, and that health services are good enough to reduce child mortality, they will have a strong incentive to have a large number of children. In many countries, little can be done until the status of women is raised, their economic contribution recognized, and their literacy increased; sometimes this has to be done in the face of centuries of tradition.

Many organizations are critical of such an approach. As is generally accepted, the population problem cannot be solved unless poverty and inequality are eliminated. Many critics argue, however, that poverty is caused by the destruction of local lifestyles that have proved themselves sustainable over a long period of time. In their view, higher economic growth, even when properly distributed, is a recipe that will not work here, either.

The Most Vulnerable Groups

The populations that are under the highest pressure are native peoples, such as the Indian peoples of the Amazon Basin, the Aboriginals of Australia and the Inuit (Eskimos) of North America. As the Brundtland Report put it:

> Growing interaction with the larger world is increasing the vulnerability of these groups, since they are often left out of the processes of economic development. Social discrimination, cultural barriers, and the exclusion of these people from national political processes make these groups vulnerable and subject to exploitation. Many groups become dispossessed

and marginalized, and their traditional practices disappear. They become the victims of what could be described as cultural extinction.

The starting point for a just and humane policy for such groups is the recognition and protection of their traditional rights to land and the other resources that sustain their way of life — rights they may define in terms that do not fit into standard legal systems.

With this, the Brundtland Commission acknowledges that the social and legal framework of many indigenous peoples differs so fundamentally from nation-state politics and legislation, which have often been modelled on Western systems, that the traditional forms of law and social organization must be recognized.

(2) Food

Since the 1950s, food production has increased dramatically. In 1950, cereal production stood at some 700 million tonnes and by 1985 this had more than doubled, to over 1,800 million tonnes. To a large extent, this increase can be attributed to new, high-yield varieties of crops, increased fertilizer use (up ninefold during this period), intensified use of pesticides (32 times as much as in 1950) and irrigation. According to FAO, this trend will continue. Food production per head of the world population is now higher than ever before. In 1985 production of cereals and root crops amounted to 500 kilograms per person. Nevertheless, 730 million people do not have enough food. There are places where too little is grown; there are places where large numbers cannot afford to buy food. And there are broad areas of the Earth, in both industrial and developing countries, where increases in food production are undermining the very basis of future production.

Hunger

The millions fleeing drought-stricken Africa are symbols of a failing agricultural policy. Since 1970, Africa has consumed more food than it has produced. In almost all the Sahel countries, population growth is outpacing food production.

Short-sighted policies are leading to degradation of the agricultural

High-rise buildings and slums in Caracas, Venezuela. (Wolf Krabel)

resource base on almost every continent: soil erosion in North America; soil acidification in Europe; deforestation and desertification in Asia, Africa, and Latin America; and waste and pollution of water almost everywhere.

The Brundtland Commission identifies four major problem areas:

- 'The food surpluses in North America and Europe result mainly from subsidies and other incentives that stimulate production even in the absence of demand. Direct or indirect subsidies, which now cover virtually the entire food cycle, have become extremely expensive. In the United States, the cost of farm support has grown from $2.7 billion in 1980 to $25.8 billion in 1986. In the EEC, such costs have risen from $6.2 billion in 1976 to $21.5 billion in 1986.'

  Food surpluses depress the prices of food products on the world market. Farmers in Third World countries cannot compete with the cheap food imported from industrialized countries, and thus lose their source of income. For the Third World countries it is often cheaper to buy European or US grain than produce it themselves, rendering it impossible to maintain an adequate domestic food production base.

- Because the interests of small producers have been neglected and priority given to large-scale, export-oriented production, many people have run into serious problems:

  'Agricultural support systems seldom take into account the special circumstances of subsistence farmers and herders. Subsistence farmers cannot afford the high cash outlay of modern inputs. Many are shifting cultivators who do not have a clear title to the land they use. They may plant a variety of crops on one plot to meet their own needs, and are thus unable to use methods developed for large stands of a single crop.

  'Many herders are nomadic and difficult to reach with education, advice, and equipment. They, like subsistence farmers, depend on certain traditional rights, which are threatened by commercial developments. Women farmers, though they play a critical role in food production, are often ignored by programmes meant to improve production.'

- Erosion is responsible for the loss of large areas of fertile land. Without conservation measures, 544 million hectares of agricultural land in Asia, Africa and Latin America will fall victim to erosion, representing a loss of almost two-thirds of present farmland in these regions. 'Erosion makes soil less able to retain water, depletes it of nutrients, and reduces the depth available for the roots to take hold. Eroded topsoil is carried to rivers, lakes, and reservoirs; silts up ports and waterways; reduces reservoir storage capacity; and increases the incidence and severity of floods.'

One of the causes mentioned by the Brundtland Commission is poorly designed irrigation. It is estimated that some 10 million hectares of irrigated land are abandoned each year as the land becomes too water-logged or saline for agriculture. What was once propagated as a cure-all for the arid regions has turned sour: the water supplied contains salt, which remains behind after rapid evaporation. The granaries of the world, such as Pakistan and the Punjab in northern India, are increasingly being transformed into salt deserts.

Another cause of erosion mentioned by the Brundtland Commission is excessive exploitation of marginal land by farmers who are no longer able to use their original, fertile lands.

- 'Chemical fertilizers and pesticides have played a large role in production increases since the Second World War, but clear warnings have been raised against over-reliance on them. The run-off of nitrogen and phosphates from excessive use of fertilizers damages water resources, and such damage is spreading.'

Chemicals used to control insects, weeds and fungi threaten the health of humans, especially children. In 1983 approximately 400,000 people in Third World countries suffered acutely from pesticide poisoning, resulting in some 10,000 deaths. Nor are the effects limited to the areas where the pesticides are applied; they pass along the food chain, all the way through to the consumer.

Measures to be Taken

'In the remaining years of this century more than a billion people will be added to the human family. To feed this family, the global food system must be managed to increase food production by three to four per cent yearly.' This will require an inconceivable effort, especially now it seems we are undermining the basis of our food production system. In the opinion of the Brundtland Commission, radical changes are needed:

Subsidies on the production of food surpluses must be abolished in the industrialized world. Perhaps land needs to be taken out of production, and perhaps it is better to decrease our use of fertilizers and other chemicals, so that we produce less 'intensively'. Prices that farmers receive for their products should be raised and stabilized. This is especially important for Third World farmers, for it will induce them to invest more in food production.

Inequitable land distribution is often a major obstacle to change. Land reforms, granting small farmers rights to land for sustainable production, are essential. In addition, alternatives must be developed for chemical fertilizers and pesticides. Governments must stimulate the use of organic fertilizers. The production and use of agrochemicals must be subjected to more stringent controls; the same holds for the exports of agricultural poisons by industrialized countries.

Natural Systems of Soil Enrichment and Pest Control

- 'Crop residues and farmyard manure are potential sources of soil nutrients;

- 'Use of organic wastes in agriculture reduces run-off of water and nutrients;

- 'Using farmyard manure, especially in conjunction with inter-cropping and crop rotation, can greatly lower production costs;

- 'Overall systems efficiency is enhanced if manure or vegetable biomass is anaerobically digested in biogas plants, yielding energy for cooking and to run pumps, motors, or electric generators;

- 'Natural systems of biological nitrogen fixation through the use of certain annual plants, trees and micro-organisms have a high potential;

- 'Integrated pest management reduces the need for agrochemicals, and releases foreign exchange for other development projects;

- 'By providing adequate information on pests, natural predators of insects, seed varieties tailored to resist pests, and integrated cropping patterns, farmers can accelerate modification of their farming practices.'

Land Use

The Brundtland Commission distinguishes three types of agricultural land:

- **'Enhancement areas**, which are capable of sustaining intensive cropping and higher population and consumption levels;

- **'Prevention areas**, which by common consent should not be developed for intensive agriculture or, where developed, should be converted to other uses;

- **'Restoration areas**, where land stripped of vegetative cover has either totally lost its productivity or had it drastically reduced.'

According to the Commission, this classification of land should form the basis of a future agricultural strategy. The prevention areas should be denied supports and subsidies for intensive agriculture. Ecologically and economically sustainable forms of grazing, forestry, fuelwood plantations, fruit farming or other production might well be stimulated in such areas, however. In the restoration areas it may even be necessary to deny people (and their herds) the use of the land. This may prove difficult because large numbers of people depend on this land for a living. Often these are precisely the people who cannot claim official rights to any land. According to the Brundtland Commission, 'selection of land for each category will demand a decision-making process in which the poor and more marginalized segments of the population are represented.'

Criticisms

Not everybody agrees with this analysis made by the Brundtland Commission. In many people's eyes, the classification into three types of agricultural land serves only to confirm and consolidate the existing situation, leaving untouched the root causes of the food problem.

Proceeding from this analysis, the most fertile areas will be used for commercial, export-oriented agriculture, which is usually capital-intensive and requires specialized know-how. The poorest segments of the Third World's population do not stand to gain much from such developments. Subsistence farmers would be relegated to the prevention areas. However, this is where the estates of the large landowners are often to be found, and there is no labour-intensive forestry and cattle breeding planned in these areas. This leaves the restoration areas, for which the Brundtland Commission suggests that population pressure should be strongly reduced, if necessary by closing them off. And where should the poor farmers go? According to Vandana Shiva, director of an environmental institute in the north of India, the Brundtland Commission forgets that in the final analysis it is not the farmers but the pursuit of profit that is to blame for the loss of fertile soil.

In an article in the international journal *The Ecologist* (No. 4/5, 1987), she illustrates this with reference to Ethiopia, whose food problems have frequently made the headlines:

> Under the Third Five Year Plan (1968–1973), Ethiopia spent only one per cent of the total expenditures on peasant agriculture and instead emphasized the development of large-scale, commercial farms producing crops for export. Tractors, pesticides, fertilizers were exempted from import duty. Multinationals making agrarian investments of $200,000 or more were given a 3 to 5 year income tax holiday. Commercial development of the Awash Valley was part of the plan. By 1970, 60 per cent of the land brought under cultivation in the Awash Valley had been devoted to cotton production, while sugar plantations claimed another 22 per cent of the cultivated area. To make way for these multinational-managed commercial farms, the government had forcibly evicted Afar pastoralists from their traditional lowland pastures. The nomads were thus compelled to use the vulnerable uphill areas. The Afars were thus pushed into the fragile uplands which were rapidly overgrazed and degraded. The degradation of the Ethiopian highlands thus needs to be viewed in the context of the introduction of commercial export agriculture in the lowlands, and the consequent displacement of nomads and peasants.

Many Third World and environmental organizations also warn against the high expectations that many (including the members of the Brundtland Commission) seem to have about a Biotechnology Revolution. Since the Second World War scientists have tried, by cross-breeding and the introduction of new genetic characteristics, to grow high-yield varieties of crops. In the sixties it was assumed that

With their century-old irrigation system, the sawahs can meet the rice requirements of densely populated regions. Indonesia. (Wolf Krabel)

these crops could make a substantial contribution in the fight against food shortages in large parts of the world. Production indeed increased substantially in subsequent years. At the same time, however, it was found that introduction of these crops was successful only in combination with large-scale fertilizer application. Moreover, the crops proved to be highly vulnerable to pests and diseases, necessitating greatly intensified use of pesticides. These agro-chemicals have had a serious impact on the environment.

For many small-scale farmers this Green Revolution proved disastrous. They could not pay for the fertilizers and pesticides; they were not even creditworthy. What the Green Revolution did achieve was to increase the profit-making potential of agriculture, making the land more attractive to rich farmers. The result: many leaseholders were evicted from their land, and small farmers bought out. The range of food products available to the people in rural areas was also affected. Farmers in Indonesia, for instance, used to keep carp in their wet rice paddies, providing a major source of protein; after the introduction of pesticides, all fish perished.

The Green Revolution has now changed into a Genetic Revolution. Genetic material from plants and animals is now being manipulated to create new species with tailor-made characteristics: cold-resistant rice, sugar cane with a high sugar and a low water content, and even cross-breeds between goats and sheep. Despite the technical differences between the two revolutions, the environmental and socio-economic objections remain unchanged.

The Hamburger Connection

'Every other day the hamburger giant McDonald's opens three new restaurants somewhere in the world: more than five hundred each year. In the year 2000 McDonald's aims to operate 15,000 outlets: 8,500 in the United States and 6,500 in the rest of the world,' according to an article in the Dutch periodical *De Kleine Aarde*. Christiane Crefe, Martin Herbst and Siegfried Pater spent several years studying the operations of the hamburger giants. Their findings are summarized below.

'The hamburger is spreading like wildfire. After McDonald's opened their first restaurant in Chicago in ➤

1955, things moved fast. By 1960 the company already had 200 restaurants, in 1968 1,000, in 1980 outlet No. 6,000 was opened in Munich, and in 1984 No. 8,000 near Atlanta in the US.'

Raw Materials

Where do such fast food chains obtain their raw materials and how does this affect the environment and the position of poor farmers? 'McDonald's itself produces nothing,' says the company's chief buyer for Europe, Michael Gerling. The raw materials are centrally purchased, standardized and distributed. John Barnes, production manager and vice-president at Burger King in Miami: 'We only deal with companies capable of supplying a product in multi-million quantities.' In the Federal Republic of Germany each day five hundred cows are processed into mincemeat for hamburgers. The hamburger is an international product. The white bread comes from Pfungstadt in West Germany, but is made from American wheat. Cheese is obtained from the Netherlands, gerkins, mustard and mayonnaise are supplied by a German company in Bavaria. The lettuce is flown in from California in winter and imported from Spain in summer. Onions are bought in the United States, potatoes in the Netherlands. The ketchup is from an American company, the raw material for the cups from Canada. The packaging material comes from Scandinavia, is printed in West Germany and cut to size in France.

Monopoly

The products are made on such a large scale, and the demands they must meet so stringent, that only mega-companies can act as suppliers to the fast food chains. The electrical group ITT has become involved in large-scale bakeries and the sale of seeds, while the transport company Greyhound has moved into meat processing. Proctor & Gamble, the chemicals and detergents giant, is investing in soya production research, and Boeing, of airplane fame, has purchased interests in potato cultivation in the north-west of the United States.

In agribusiness, competition has been all but eliminated. The results: soaring profits for the companies involved. Today, one quarter of the American food industry is responsible for 75 per cent of profits and for 90 per cent of food commercials on national TV.

The Rain Forests

Between 1960 and 1976, beef consumption per head of the North American population increased from 38 to 61 kilos a year. This led to price rises and the meat companies started looking for cheap beef in other countries. The rain forests of Central America proved to hold out excellent prospects as pastureland. One of the Central American countries is Costa Rica. 'Each year 50,000 to 70,000 hectares of forest are destroyed, and much of this only to make space for cattle ranching,' says Alexander Bonilla, geologist, environmental expert and chairman of Costa Rica's Ecological Party. More than one third of the country is already pasture. Still, meat consumption by the Costa Ricans themselves is decreasing, for the meat is for the export market. Ninety-five per cent of meat production is exported to the United States, most of it ending up in the fast food chains. Meanwhile, the poor farmers are starving. 'Where big cattle ranches are established, we have to go. There hunger is our share,' they say. After coffee and bananas, beef now comes third on the list of Costa Rica's export products. The prices of these exports are low compared with those of agricultural imports such as grain, fruit, vegetables and cattle feed, which are continually rising. Foreign debts and expensive imports force the country to continually increase its exports. The clearing of rain forests to convert them into pastures for

⇨ 'hamburger cows' is fully in line with this development.
It is creating an even less equitable land distribution
than ten years ago, when 60 per cent of the peasant
families possessed only four per cent of the land under
cultivation, with 0.1 per cent of the land owners holding
over twenty per cent of the land.

Soya and Tapioca

In Europe, too, meat production is rising rapidly. West
Germany, for instance, uses only domestic beef for its
hamburgers. To meet demand, the cows are fed
concentrates. Grass alone is no longer enough; for in
winter, too, demand for meat is high. In intensive
factory-farming, hundreds of cows or pigs or many
thousands of chickens are kept in automated sheds. A
large part of the fodder used is obtained from developing
countries: soya from Brazil, or tapioca from Thailand. In
addition, green maize is increasingly being grown as
fodder. The consequences for the inhabitants of the
developing countries and for their environment are
disastrous.

The Third World

Soya supplies from Brazil meet 30 per cent of the
European Community's demand. Since 1965, the soya
growing area has increased twentyfold, from 432,000
hectares to nine million hectares. This represents some
18 per cent of Brazil's agricultural land base. A study by
the University of Sao Paulo on the major farming areas
in the southern states of Sao Paulo, Parana and Rio
Grande do Sul in the years of headlong soya
development (1970–1973) revealed that 88 per cent of
the soya was grown on land that as a rule had formerly
been used for labour-intensive food crops, such as rice,
beans, manioc, potatoes and onions, or for dairy cows or
pigs. Where previously seven to eight labourers were

➡

employed in growing produce for the local market, now
only one is needed for tending the soya that helps the
European Community produce meat and milk surpluses.
Soya cultivation is dominated by a handful of American,
Dutch, French, German and Swiss companies.

Europe

In Western Europe, countries like the Netherlands,
Belgium, West Germany and Denmark produce large
quantities of meat, partly for the export market. The
conversion of vegetable to animal protein, embodied in
the fattening of chickens, pigs and cows, constitutes a
highly inefficient process in which 80 per cent of
available proteins are lost. In the Netherlands three-
quarters of farmland is used for fodder production; even
so, cattle breeding is so intensive that fodder must also
be imported. For each hectare of agricultural land in the
Netherlands devoted to large-scale, highly intensive
cattle breeding, two to three hectares are required in
other countries, mainly for soya and tapioca production.
Per capita, the Dutch use twice as much farmland as the
average for the world as a whole. If the same
consumption pattern were adopted worldwide, we would
need another earth, only without people! No wonder,
then, that the environmental organizations that compiled
these facts and figures advocate a drastic reduction of
meat production and consumption.

Acid Rain

In the industrialized world the environmental
consequences of this meat culture are clearly visible, in
the form of manure surpluses, for instance. Much of
what is eaten by cows, pigs and other animals comes out
again at the other end. In several West European
regions, the ammonia contained in the excrement is a
major component of acid rain, causing widespread death

⇨

of woods and heathland.

The hamburger industry is thus responsible not only for destruction of tropical rain forests in Latin America. In Western Europe, too, woods are dying on account of meat production. Production of green maize as a cattle diet supplement is expanding rapidly. Maize can withstand large amounts of manure, and maize fields are increasingly being used as dumping grounds for manure surpluses. Because of the large amounts of manure and agrichemicals used, maize monocultures give rise to soil erosion and groundwater contamination.

Food Culture

'We educate people, giving them a completely new life style. We'll open up every country in the world. China? There alone, one billion hungry people are waiting for us.' These are the words of a representative of the fast food industry. Environmental and Third World organizations advocate an entirely different food culture. Their plea is for reinforcement of sustainable, organic agriculture, serving mainly local and regional markets, and reduction of the use of chemicals. This will yield ecologically sound food. Perhaps the price will be somewhat higher, but this we owe to our farmers, here and in the Third World, to our environment, and to future generations.

(3) Ecosystems and Nature Conservation

FAO figures indicate that the world loses 100,000 square kilometres of tropical forest each year. That figure does not, however, take into account those forests that have been cleared and have regrown into degraded forests. If this is included, the figure doubles. If destruction continues at this pace, the world will be without tropical forests in fifty years from now, well within the lifetime of a child born today. The environmental magazine, *The Ecologist* (No. 4/5, 1987), in an editorial described the effects this would have.

Acid rain effect on Regency architecture. Cotswold limestone. (Mike Jackson/Environmental Picture Library)

Forest destruction spells cultural death for the estimated 140 million people who at present live in the forests, either as hunter-gatherers, or as swidden agriculturalists or by extracting the produce of the forest on a sustainable basis. Many of these people rely on the forest for their entire livelihood. They derive from it the building materials for their houses; the wood for their agricultural implements; the herbs for their traditional medicines; the fibres and dyes for their clothes; and the materials for their traditional religious and cultural artefacts. But the forest is not simply the source of material benefits. It is the foundation on which the very cultures of forest peoples are built, the resting place of their ancestors and the home of their deities. In effect, for the world's forest dwellers, the destruction of tropical forests amounts to nothing less than ethnocide, murdering entire peoples, with their cultures, their religions and all that belongs to them.

Species

The number of plant and animal species on Earth is estimated to be between five and thirty million. Only 1.7 million of these have been identified or studied in any depth. The majority, 50 but perhaps even 90 per cent, are to be found in the humid forests of the tropics. These forests contain an inconceivable number of species. Ninety per cent of all primate species live in the tropical rain forests, together with two-thirds of all known plants, 40 per cent of birds of prey and 80 per cent of insects. The Amazon jungle houses an estimated one million different animals and plants, including 2,500 tree species, 1,800 bird species and 2,000 fish species. One single hectare of the rain forest may support 400 trees, each one a different species. As a comparison, an average forest in the temperate zone has no more than ten to fifteen species of tree per hectare. A single river in Brazil was found to support more species of fish than all the rivers in the United States combined.

In the words of the Brundtland Commission:

> The diversity of species is necessary for the normal functioning of ecosystems and the biosphere as a whole. The genetic material in wild species contributes billions of dollars yearly to the world economy in the form of improved crop species, new drugs and medicines, and raw materials for industry. But utility aside, there are also moral, ethical, cultural, aesthetic, and purely scientific reasons for conserving wild beings.

Causes

Several major causes of ecosystem destruction are identified by the

Brundtland Commission. In the first place, farmers in the tropics are perceived as being forced to use their land in an inefficient way, for instance without fertilizers or employing low-yield crops. In this way, excessively large areas of farmland are required. The second cause singled out by the Commission is population growth. 'Brazil, Colombia, the Ivory Coast, Indonesia, Kenya, Madagascar, Peru, the Philippines, Thailand and other nations suffer a massive flow of farmers from traditional homelands into virgin territories. These areas are perceived by the migrants as "free" lands available for unimpeded settlement,' according to the Brundtland Report. Lastly, the Commission refers to commercial logging and large-scale, low-yield cattle breeding in tropical forest areas as major causes of destruction.

Measures Recommended

One of the measures proposed by the Brundtland Commission is to close off huge reserves. In 1985 there were about 3,000 protected nature reserves, covering a total area of more than 400 million hectares, approximately the size of Western Europe. According to conservationists, the area designated as nature reserve must be at least trebled if we are to preserve all species. The Brundtland Commission proposes an international agreement providing for the protection of species. In addition, it advocates development of a National Conservation Strategy by every country of the world.

Tropical Forests Action Plan

One of the plans receiving strong support from the Brundtland Commission is *Tropical Forests: A Call for Action*. This Plan, drawn up by the World Resources Institute in co-operation with the World Bank and the United Nations Development Programme (UNDP), proposes a five-year, $8 billion action programme aimed at the production of fuelwood, commercial forestry, reforestation and preservation of tropical forest systems. Many industrialized countries are supporting this Plan.

An Alternative

The reactions of environmental and Third World organizations to *A*

Call for Action varied widely. Some rejected the Plan outright, disagreeing entirely with the approach taken by the World Bank and the United Nations — 'the view from Washington'. Others supported it, in the hope that these powerful organizations might bring about a change for the better. According to Vandana Shiva, a widely respected spokeswoman of environmental and Third World groups, the problem has been analysed incorrectly in the Plan. She quotes the World Resources Institute, which states that: 'It is the rural poor themselves who are the primary agents of destruction as they clear forests for agriculture, fuelwood and other necessities. Lacking other means to meet their daily survival needs, rural people are forced to steadily erode the capacity of their natural environment to support them.'

Two Views of the Forest Crisis

	The View from Washington	The View from the People
Who destroys the forests?	People destroy forests	Profits destroy forests
Who is a tropical forest expert?	Scientific knowledge of tropical forestry exists only with experts in the aid-giving countries of the North	Women, peasants, forest dwellers are the best experts in tropical forestry and ecology. Expatriate experts are trained only in a particular forestry science which caters to markets and works against people and nature
What is the most effective means for solving the bio-mass crisis of the poor?	Privatization is the most efficient mechanism for providing biomass to the poor	Privatization erodes the access and entitlements of the poorest to land and biomass
What is the most effective mechanism for ecological recovery?	Commercial criteria (inc. profits) can be an exclusive and effective guide to ecological rehabilitation	Exclusive concern with profitability has caused ecological destruction and therefore cannot reverse it. Afforestation programmes based on profitability alone can become ecological hazards in themselves

From: 'Forestry, Myths and the World Bank: A Critical Review of *Tropical Forests: A Call for Action*', by Vandana Shiva, *The Ecologist*, Vol. 17, No. 4/5, 1987.

Oil recovery in Lake Maracaibo, Venezuela. (Wolf Krabel)

Vandana Shiva is furious about what she calls a 'number of very seductive myths'. In her view those responsible for forest destruction are the very organizations propagating such myths. Large-scale agriculture, as practised in Ethiopia, is a major cause of deforestation. In Central America, cattle breeding is responsible for deforestation of two-thirds of the region. In Brazil, 60 per cent of deforestation between 1966 and 1975 was caused by large-scale cattle breeding and road construction. Dams are another major cause of forest destruction. In Brazil about 216,000 hectares of tropical forest were flooded for the Tucurui project. In the northern part of the Amazon region, the Balbina dam will destroy some 2,346 square kilometres of tropical forest. Many of the farmers moving into the tropical forests do not go there of their own accord. In Indonesia, more than 3.6 million Javanese farmers have been sent into the dense forests of the sparsely populated islands of the archipelago as part of the government's 'transmigration programme'. This programme threatens the existence of at least 3.3 million hectares of tropical rain forest. In Brazil, similar colonization methods were responsible for 17 per cent of the forest destruction that took place between 1966 and 1975. All these activities were financed by major financial institutions such as the World Bank. Vandana Shiva, and many others, do not hold out high expectations for forestry as practised by these institutions. Often, the effect is the very opposite of what was intended, for instance because trees are planted that are useful only to the paper-making industry, such as the rapidly growing but ecologically destructive Eucalyptus tree.

The Sarawak Timber Blockade

Deep in the Sarawak jungle, native peoples are blocking the roads used by the timber companies. The blockade started in March 1987, closing the roads in large parts of this East Malaysian state. Some months previously I visited the area.

When we arrive it is already late. The trip through the jungle has taken a long time, and we kept on losing our way. At last we reach the bridge where we are supposed to meet the forest people, the Penan. The river meanders through the green valley. All around us we hear the sounds of birds, monkeys and insects, and the air is hot, saturated with moisture. Harrison, a young Kayan who

➡

is in charge of the local office of Sahabat Alam Malaysia [Friends of the Earth, Malaysia], leads the way. Shrill shrieks resound in the forest, and a short while later we stand face to face with the last true forest nomads of the island, muscular people, carrying blowpipes and spears. After half an hour's walk we reach a camp. It is as if we have arrived at a jungle slum. The huts are sagging, mangy dogs howl at us. Corrugated roofs keep the heat trapped inside. The headman shakes hands with us, saying: 'This is not the way we want to live. We are people of the forest. We have never had any fixed abode, we moved around to stay alive. We are hunters, we need game. Tree felling has made this impossible. Now we cannot shoot enough to stay alive and we have to sow rice and work for the foresters to survive.'

A woman continues: 'They mowed down our forest and desecrated the graves of our forefathers. Our water is being polluted and our plants destroyed. The lumberjacks kill the animals in the forest or chase them away. The forest provides us wild sago and fruits for food, ten kinds of wood for our blowpipes and many different plants as medicines for headaches, sprains, wounds and other ailments. We women gather *uwai* (rattan) and *daun* (leaves) to make our shelters and baskets. The forest is our source of survival. Without the forest we'll all be dead and now there's hardly anything left.'

We spend the night in a room that the Penan use for a church service the next day. It seems the missionaries have done a thorough job here; Christianity has found its way deep into the rain forest. The next day we travel into this jungle, by boat. Trees tower high into the sky, adorned with ferns and orchids. Snakes coil through the water as we pull the boat through one of the many rapids. Every few hundred metres the safety catch of the boat hits a rock. It is already dark when we arrive at the longhouse, the traditional communal house of the Dayak. Insect sounds from the jungle form a background buzz. The headman welcomes us as old friends. One of our company is a lawyer of the

⇨

Consumers Association of Penang (CAP). She is one of the first lawyers to penetrate this far into the jungle in order to defend the rights of the indigenous people.

That night Penan run through the jungle to other longhouses, to spread the news of our arrival. The following evening people from all around come together for a meeting. The candlelight attracts giant insects, but this does not detract from the discussion. Tension can be read on everyone's face. The problem of this community, like that of almost all the other communities here, is that commercial tree felling brings massive destruction. The native people do not know how to stop this. The timber merchants carry official documents, from which it would appear that the land is theirs. Headmen are set up against one another. In some cases the communities receive a pittance by way of compensation — some thousands of dollars for a forest worth millions. Our lawyer studies the contract and explains how the people can start legal proceedings. It is going to be a long road, and hopefully there will be some forest left by the time they reach the end.

Tree felling in Sarawak

At the heart of the conflict is control and use of the oldest, richest rain forest in the world. The island jungle contains the world's largest diversity of plants and animals. And it is being felled at an enormous pace. In 1985 alone 270,000 hectares of Sarawak forest were destroyed. If this continues at the same rate, in fifteen years there will be no forest left. The effects are plainly visible. The climate is changing. The year 1981 brought the first serious drought. Millions of gallons of water had to be brought to the affected areas. In 1983 there was another drought, and in 1986 there were even two periods of drought. In addition to droughts there are also regular floods, for many of the plant roots that retained the water have disappeared. In 1979 large parts of Sarawak were flooded. In January 1984 towns were flooded, and in 1985 the same happened again.

➡

Exports

The timber is sold, mainly to Japan and the countries of the European Community. One of the largest importers of tropical hardwood from Sarawak is the Netherlands. Increasingly, door posts, window frames and other building elements are being manufactured of hardwood.

Action

Sarawak's indigenous people went into action. In March 1987 thousands of them formed human barricades across logging tracks to stop the timber companies moving in. It worked. In many places tree felling was discontinued. Publicity and international support rendered it difficult for the Malaysian government to use force to break through the blockades. For months the Penan stayed at their positions, often dug into the forest soil. They were supported by local communities, who supplied food, and by tribe members, who often travelled hundreds of kilometres through the forest to take their turn at the blockades. In the end the government reacted with tough repression. Many Penan were arrested, and the blockades forcibly removed. People from Sahabat Alam Malaysia, such as Harrison, and from the Consumers Association of Penang, were thrown into jail. There was an outcry from environmental and Third World organizations all over the world. At last, the silent death of a unique people and their jungle received international media attention.

In a growing number of countries importing tropical timber, consumer boycotts have been started. The timber trade, under pressure from citizen movements, has begun to look for alternatives.

Some people say we are against 'development' if we do not agree to move out of our land and forest. This completely misrepresents our position. 'Development' does not mean stealing our land and forest away from us. This is not development but theft of our land, our rights and cultural

⇒

identity. 'Development' to us means:
a) recognition of our land rights in practice;
b) putting a stop to logging on our lands and forests so that
we can continue to live;
c) introducing clean water supplies, proper health facilities,
better schools for our children.
This kind of development we want. Why don't you give us
this development and progress?

There are people who say that our blockades are illegal.
However, we wish to state that we are only defending our
own land rights. The law permits people to defend their
property. Until the question of our land rights is resolved
by the government and courts, we appeal to the police not
to just take the side of the timber companies. We are
confident that the police act to safeguard people who are
weak and exploited. We appeal to the police not to arrest us
who are quietly safeguarding our land and our forest in a
peaceful manner.

Also to mislead the public, many politicians have said our
actions are directed by outsiders, foreigners and politicians.
This is not true and also insults our own intelligence and
our capacity to think and act for ourselves. These problems
have become so unbearable in the past few years that we are
forced to act. But we also welcome and accept any support
given to us by our friends, including lawyers who want to give
us legal aid, Sahabat Alam Malaysia, and other social
groups, journalists, government officials and Ministers who
have pledged to help us.

From: A declaration by 61 leaders on behalf of 27 communities of several
Malaysian peoples.   ■

(4) Energy

Energy is necessary for daily survival. Future development crucially
depends on its long-term availability in increasing quantities from sources
that are dependable, safe and environmentally sound. At present, no single
source or mix of sources is at hand to meet this future need.

According to the analysis of the Brundtland Commission, four key
elements of sustainability must be reconciled:

Environmentally benign energy supplied by windmills, Ijsselmeer, Netherlands. (Michiel Wijnbergh)

- Sufficient growth of energy supplies to meet human needs (which means accommodating a minimum of three per cent per capita income growth in developing countries);

- Energy efficiency and conservation measures, so that waste of primary energy sources is minimized;

- Public health, recognizing the problems of risks to safety inherent in a variety of energy sources;

- Protection of the biosphere and prevention of more localized forms of pollution.

Energy and the Economy

The growth of energy demand in response to industrialization, urbanization, and societal affluence has led to an extremely uneven global distribution of primary energy consumption. The consumption of energy per person in industrial market economies is more than 80 times greater than in Sub-Saharan Africa. And about a quarter of the world's population consumes three-quarters of the world's primary energy.

We are confronted with a major dilemma:

To bring developing countries' energy up to industrialized country levels by the year 2025 would require increasing present global energy use by a factor of five. The planetary ecosystem could not stand this, especially if the increases were based on non-renewable fossil fuels. Threats of global warming and acidification of the environment most probably rule out even a doubling of energy use based on present mixes of primary sources.

In short, the energy sources now being used are so polluting that we are in fact already using them on far too great a scale. If Third World countries were to use as much energy as the industrialized countries, the planet would simply not survive.

Optimism

Our energy situation forms one of the major focuses of present-day research. A growing number of studies conclude that it is possible to conserve substantial quantities of energy. An enormous amount of energy is squandered through inefficient use. We do not properly insulate our homes, we move around in petrol-guzzling cars, we use washing machines whose energy consumption is four to eight times too high. If all forms of energy consumption are listed and the most appropriate and efficient conservation techniques selected, we find that unprecedented savings can be achieved.

José Goldenberg, president of Sao Paulo's electricity utility, in 1985 told the Brundtland Commission:

> We must change our attitude towards consumer goods in developing countries and we must create technological advances that will allow us to carry on economic development using less energy. We must ask ourselves can we solve the problems of underdevelopment without using or increasing the tremendous amount of energy used by these countries. The idea that developing countries use very little energy is an incorrect idea. We find that the poorest countries of all have a different problem; their problem is inefficient use of energy. Medium-income countries, such as Brazil, use more efficient and modern sources of fuel. The great hope for these countries is that the future will be built not based on technologies of the past, but using advanced technology. This will allow them to leap forward in relation to countries that are already developed.

In Brazil it has been shown that with a total investment of only four billion dollars in more efficient technologies, applied in such areas as refrigerators, street lighting and motors, energy savings in excess of 21,000 megawatts can be achieved — more than the total amount of energy used by a heavily industrialized country like the Netherlands. This corresponds to savings of $19 billion in the period from 1986 to 2000. Evidently, it is possible to achieve enormous savings through the use of efficient technologies. If these 21,000 megawatts of energy, to be produced chiefly by hydro-power, need not be generated, no new dams would have to be constructed. As a result, the lives of the Indians and rubber tappers of the Amazon Basin would not be further endangered, while hundreds of thousands of hectares of tropical rain forest need not disappear. Unfortunately, this has not yet turned into reality. As yet, the ideas of José Goldenberg, and of many others, have scarcely been put into practice.

Nuclear Power

The Brundtland Commission is critical of nuclear power:

> And now, after almost four decades of immense technological effort to

support nuclear development, nuclear energy has become widely used. However, during this period of practical experience with building and running nuclear reactors, the nature of the costs, risks, and benefits have become much more evident, and, as such, the subject of sharp controversy. Worldwide, countries hold different views on nuclear energy. The discussion in the Commission also reflected these tendencies, views and positions. Yet all agreed that the generation of nuclear power is only justifiable if there are solid solutions to the presently unsolved problems to which it gives rise. The highest priority must be accorded to research and development on environmentally sound and economically viable alternatives, as well as on means of increasing the safety of nuclear energy.

Unfortunately, the Brundtland Commission could not agree on a clear yes or no to nuclear power.

For environmental activists the world over, nuclear power has always been a major focus of attention. In their view, this relatively new technology brings with it such a complex of serious health, safety and environmental problems as to be unacceptable as a means of electrical power generation. From the beginning to the end, the chain of production and processing facilities required to tap this source of energy releases large quantities of radioactive (and chemical) poisons into the environment. At each stage, there are still serious problems with waste management, even under 'normal' operating conditions. In the event of an accident, even larger areas of land may become contaminated with radioactive fall-out.

To most environmentalists, it is not only the nuclear power plants themselves or the waste-processing facilities that form an unacceptable hazard. The long-term storage of high-level radioactive waste — and indeed the 'storage' of nuclear buildings and facilities that have been shut down — is bound to involve the release of harmful radiation. In and around the uranium mines, too, many people are exposed to the radioactive gases released when the ore is unlocked from the ground, as is described later in this book.

Another major objection voiced against nuclear technology is that the products and processes employed can be equally well used for nuclear weapons. Uranium, plutonium and tritium are the three key materials for thermonuclear bombs. Their flows through the 'civilian' and military fuel cycles are a matter of secrecy, but there is sufficient evidence that these flows are very much interlinked. Especially in view of the Brundtland Commission's conclusions about the threats of escalating arms races and nuclear war, their indecision on the issue of nuclear power reflects the conflicting interests prevailing in the world.

Fossil Fuels

The Brundtland Commission warns about the hazards not only of nuclear power but also of burning fossil fuels such as coal, oil and gas. In their view, the main danger of the latter lies in the 'greenhouse effect'. Coal, oil and gas are in fact plant residues. It took millions of years to build up these energy reserves from dying plants. In this process, carbon dioxide was consumed and oxygen produced. The carbon dioxide fixed in these enormous reserves is now being rapidly released. The concentration of carbon dioxide in our atmosphere is again rising. Carbon dioxide, together with several other gases, retains heat, acting as a kind of global insulation. Without these gases, the Earth would be very cold indeed. Today, however, we are producing far too much of this insulation material. This will cause the temperature on Earth to rise, most probably with disastrous consequences. Productive agricultural areas will dry out, forests will die, rising sea levels will flood coastal areas and weather patterns will be disrupted. The only way we can prevent this scenario unfolding is by dramatically reducing the use of fossil energy, by aiming for maximum energy efficiency and conservation and by accelerated introduction of alternative, sustainable sources of energy.

The Greenhouse Effect

In fifty years time, the world will be a different place. As a result of the increased amount of carbon dioxide and other gases in the atmosphere, the average temperature on Earth has risen dramatically. In the temperate and cold zones it is as much as five to eight degrees Celsius warmer. Because of changed wind and rainfall patterns, traditional dynamics of weather have been disrupted. Hurricanes are more frequent and severe, while previously moist regions suffer prolonged droughts.

Higher temperatures have caused sea levels to rise the world over. Some countries have been able to raise their dikes and construct other flood-control facilities protecting them against the rising tides. But in the Third World, especially, where no money is available for such measures, the rising seas have created disastrous situations. Towns are flooded and important coastal

➡

⇨

farming regions have silted up completely. Millions of people have drowned or have had to flee their homes.

The climatic change occurred so suddenly that there is not a single agricultural system that is still functioning as it should. Droughts and flash floods have destroyed entire harvests. This has resulted in famines, not only in Africa, Latin America and Asia, but also in the industrialized world. Yields from the 'bread baskets' of the United States and the Soviet Union have all but collapsed. The world is awaiting the great disaster that is still to come. Gigantic sections of the Antarctic icepack threaten to break loose, the most likely cause being melting of the bottom surface of the ice layer resting on the sea bed. Possibly the sea level will rise by five to eight metres within a few decades. If it does, people living in the coastal areas of rich countries will also have to move if they want to keep their feet dry.

There will in, say, fifty years time be heated discussions on this awful predicament. By then, however, there will be little that can be done, for the gases we have allowed to enter the atmosphere in the preceding two centuries will not disappear overnight. That will take hundreds of years.

This scenario is not based on fantasy. It is a prediction, which the International Council of Scientific Unions considers 'plausible and probable'. The main causes are the increased production of carbon dioxide, chlorofluorocarbons (CFCs), methane, ozone and nitrous oxide (laughing gas) and the continuing destruction of forests and other natural vegetation the world over.

Carbon Dioxide

Before the Industrial Revolution, more than two centuries ago, the carbon dioxide concentration was about 280 parts per million parts of air. By 1980 this had increased to 340 parts, and by the middle of the next century it will have doubled to 560 parts — unless we

➡

take far-reaching measures. Coal-burning is the major source of this carbon dioxide. In this respect, oil and especially natural gas are much cleaner fuels, for their combustion energy is derived to a large extent from water formation. The doubling of the carbon dioxide concentration will cause the Earth's mean temperature to rise by 1.5 to 4.5 degrees Celsius — an estimate with a high degree of uncertainty. No one knows exactly how the climate will react, whether there will be more clouds, how the oceans will change. Near the equator the rise in temperature will be well below the mean. In temperate zones, it will exceed the mean, and near the poles the increase may be as high as four to eight degrees Celsius.

Other 'Greenhouse Gases'

What is much less widely known is that other gases — nitrous oxides, methane and freons (chloro-fluorocarbons, or CFCs) — are also major contributors to the greenhouse effect. CFCs are also considered to be the main cause of depletion of the ozone layer in the stratosphere, as discussed below. The methane concentration in the atmosphere is currently increasing at a rate of one half to two per cent a year. The concentration of freons is rising by five to six per cent a year; that of nitrous oxides by 0.2 to 0.3 per cent. These extra gases may have an enormous effect. Lucas Reijnders, a respected Dutch environmentalist, reports that computer models predict that, if these trends are allowed to continue, the temperature will rise by 80 degrees Celsius! Proceeding from much more moderate assumptions, freons, methane and nitrous oxides together are expected to produce a temperature rise of 1.5 to 4.5 degrees Celsius. Lucas Reijnders concludes that: 'If things do not change, an average temperature rise of at least 3 to 9 degrees Celsius in less than one hundred years' time is to be reckoned with. At our latitude, the rise will be well above the average, and at the poles it might increase by 8 to 10 degrees Celsius.'

⇨

Deforestation and Modern Agriculture

For their growth, trees and other green plants utilize the
carbon dioxide in the air. The vegetative cover of the
Earth thus constitutes a key element in Nature's
maintenance of a healthy atmosphere. The tropical
rain forests, in particular, fulfil a vital role. However, as
we have seen, these forests are being destroyed at an
alarming rate. The same applies to many other forms of
natural vegetation. Thus, not only is more and more
carbon dioxide being produced; Nature's way of re-
using it is also being systematically undermined.

In this context, modern agriculture is a major
contributor to the greenhouse effect: by draining and
clearing lands considered unproductive, the carbon
trapped in the vegetation and humus is released as
carbon dioxide. In addition, intensive agriculture
employs massive quantities of chemical fertilizers and
pesticides, which are produced in energy-intensive
industries that contribute to the emission of carbon
dioxide.

Measures

These disastrous developments must be stopped. And
they can be stopped. The Brundtland Commission
proposes energy conservation and alternative energy
sources as solutions. The production of freons is to be
restricted. There is no time to wait until the greenhouse
effects have been studied in all their ramifications. By
then, it will be too late. The Brundtland Commission,
however, did not prove capable of drawing firm
conclusions from the hard data. But it is high time to do
so, as witness the above. Environmentalists conclude
that there are a number of steps that must be urgently
taken: far more energy conservation measures; a massive
reduction of fossil-fuel combustion and an end to
construction of coal-fired power plants; a dramatic
reduction of chlorofluorocarbon emissions and

➡

establishment of a recycling system for freons used as refrigerants in domestic fridges and other products; and regional reforestation programmes designed and implemented by local populations. These measures would also achieve much needed improvements in air quality, ozone layer integrity, equity of land use and nature conservation as a whole.

The Fuelwood Crisis

Perhaps of far greater impact than the commercial energy crisis is the shortage of fuelwood in the world. According to the Brundtland Report:

> Seventy per cent of the people in developing countries use wood and burn between 350 and 2,900 kilograms of dry wood annually per person. Wood is being consumed in greater quantities than it can regrow in many Third World countries. Most people in these countries use biomass — in the form of wood, charcoal, dung and crop residues — for cooking, for heating their dwellings, and even for lighting. The Food and Agriculture Organization's estimates suggest that in 1980 around 1.3 billion people lived in wood-deficit areas. If this overharvesting continues at present rates, by the year 2000 some 2.4 billion people may be living in areas where firewood is acutely scarce or has to be obtained elsewhere.

> When fuelwood is in short supply, people normally economize; when it is no longer available, rural people are forced to burn such fuels as cow dung, crop stems and husks, and weeds. Often this does no harm, since waste products are used. But the burning of dung and certain crop residues may in some cases rob the soil of needed nutrients. Eventually extreme fuel shortages can reduce the number of cooked meals and shorten the cooking time, which increases malnourishment.

The fuelwood crisis does not affect only rural areas, however:

> Many urban people rely on wood as well, and most of this has to be purchased, while in rural areas it can usually be collected. Recently, as the price of wood fuels has been rising, poor families have been obliged to spend increasing proportions of their income on wood. In Addis Ababa and Maputo, families may spend a third to half of their incomes this way.

Dead trees, Kent. (Philip Carr/Environmental Picture Library)

Fuel-efficient Stoves

People in Third World countries often use open fires for cooking, so that much of the heat is lost. In the past ten years, however, plenty of research and development has been carried out on stoves utilizing an efficient wood combustion process. The Brundtland Commission recommends accelerated introduction of these modern stoves. Whether they are indeed as useful as they appear is not entirely clear. On the assumption that cleverly devised stoves may alleviate the fuelwood crisis, hundreds of different designs have been introduced in many Third World countries. In a number of cases satisfactory results have indeed been achieved. However, though the programmes for introduction of energy-efficient stoves have hardly been evaluated, in several cases such stoves have been found to consume *more* energy than in the original situation. Often this was because the stoves did not meet the requirements of the users, who had not been involved in the design process. Wood may in fact be burnt in a very clean and efficient way, but sometimes combustion proceeds too quickly, so that for meals requiring long cooking much more fuelwood is needed than was originally the case. The materials from which the stoves are constructed are not always appropriate to the Third World situation either. Furthermore, simply shielding a wood fire from draughts and wind may often raise its efficiency so spectacularly as to do away with the need for special stoves. All too often, in any case, these stoves find their way only to a very small section of the population, and seldom the poorest.

Forestry

The Brundtland Commission makes a plea for large-scale reforestation. Some of the problems connected with the Commission's 'top-down' approach have been indicated in the preceding chapters. Here, too, the Brundtland Commission shows that it considers the poor farmers to be responsible for deforestation:

> To most farmers, especially the poor ones, wood is a 'free good' until the last available tree is cut down. Rural areas require totally different strategies than urban areas. Given the basic need for domestic fuel, and the few substitutes available, it seems that the only way out of this problem in the short and medium term is to treat fuelwood like food and grow it as a subsistence crop. This is best done through employing agroforestry techniques.

To date, however, such techniques have yielded hardly any fuelwood for the poor. In most cases the large-scale plantations provide fibres for industry or fuelwood for urban areas. Wood from the plantations costs money, and that is precisely what the poorest, landless farmers do not have.

However, the Brundtland Commission is not unequivocal as to the causes of deforestation. One moment it accuses the poor farmers: 'programmes to preserve forest resources must start with the local people who are both victims and agents of destruction'; and the next it points to a different cause: 'The fuelwood crisis and deforestation — although related — are not the same problems. Wood fuels destined for urban and industrial consumers do tend to come from forests. But only a small proportion of that used by the rural poor comes from forests. Even in these cases, villagers rarely chop down trees; most collect dead branches or cut them from trees.'

Environmental and Third World organizations point out that the causes are often the same as those underlying the food problem. Deforestation is usually caused by large-scale developments, such as the international timber trade or commercial, export-oriented agriculture. Subsistence farmers flee to the marginal land, where there is simply not enough wood to survive.

(5) Industrialization

> Industry is central to the economies of modern societies and an indispensable motor of growth. It is essential to developing countries to widen their development base and meet growing needs. And though industrialized countries are said to be moving into a post-industrial, information-based era, this shift must be powered by a continuing flow of wealth from industry.

So states the Brundtland Commission.

While warning against the effects of industrial growth, the Commission nevertheless calls for an enormous growth of industrial production.

> If industrial development is to be sustainable over the long term, it will have to change radically in terms of the quality of that development, particularly in industrialized countries. But this is not to suggest that industrialization has reached a quantitative limit. Even today, according to

the United Nations, world consumption of manufactured goods would have to be increased by a factor of 2.6 if consumption of manufactured goods in developing countries were to be raised to current industrial country levels. Given expected population growth, a five- to tenfold increase in world industrial output can be anticipated by the time world population stabilizes sometime in the next century.

The Facts

In 1950 industrial output was less than one seventh of what it is today. Between 1950 and 1973 production increased rapidly, by seven per cent annually in industry and by five per cent in mining. Since that time, growth has declined somewhat — about three per cent for industry between 1973 and 1985, and no growth at all in the mining sector. Exports from Third World countries have increased enormously, including mining. The chemical industry now accounts for 10 per cent of world trade. This involves the production of some 80,000 different chemicals for commercial use (and for their production, about five million chemicals are first produced on a laboratory scale). Each year, one to two thousand new chemicals are launched on the market. In 1979, of all commercial chemicals about 1,500 were active ingredients of pesticides, 4,000 were used in medicines, and 5,500 were applied as food additives.

Hazards

Very little is known of the health effects of the 65,725 chemicals that are in common use. The Brundtland Commission quotes the US National Research Council, which found that complete health hazard evaluations were available for only 10 per cent of pesticides and 18 per cent of drugs. For nearly 80 per cent of the chemicals on the market, absolutely no toxicity data are available. Slowly, this situation is now changing. The Brundtland Commission records that:

> By 1986 more than 500 chemicals and chemical products had been banned altogether or had their uses severely restricted in the country of origin. In addition, an unknown number of chemicals are withdrawn from clearance processes every year in the light of control agency concerns, or are never submitted to national control agencies for clearance. Some of these end up in the export market.

If exports of these chemicals are to be prevented, the developing countries must receive special support. 'Third World importers have no way to effectively control trade in chemicals that have been banned or severely restricted in exporting countries. Thus these countries badly need the infrastructure to assess the risks associated with chemical use.'

The Commission therefore recommends that all governments, particularly those of the major chemical-producing countries, should:

- 'Undertake that no new chemicals be placed on international markets until the health and environmental impacts have been tested and assessed;

- 'Reinforce on-going efforts to obtain international agreement on the selection of existing chemicals for priority testing, on criteria and procedures for their assessment, and on a system for international sharing of the tasks and the resources required for this gigantic operation;

- 'Strictly regulate the export to developing countries of those chemicals for which authorization for domestic sale has not been sought or given, by increased information exchange with Third World countries;

- 'Reinforce existing regional organizations qualified to process and assess such information and to advise governments in the region on the risks associated with the use of these chemicals.'

Hazardous Wastes

It is almost impossible to quantify the amount of toxic waste produced worldwide. The majority of such waste is generated in the industrialized countries. Estimates ranging from 325 to 375 million tonnes a year provide some indication of the quantities involved, but the true volume might well be several times higher. This is an issue of grave concern to the Brundtland Commission:

In the industrialized countries certainly thousands of waste disposal sites exist, many of which are likely to require some form of remedial action. Clean-up is expensive: estimates include $10 billion for the Federal Republic of Germany, more than $1.5 billion for the Netherlands, $20–100 billion for the United States, and at least $60 million for Denmark (in 1986 US dollars).

Cleaning up wastes is one thing, but according to the Brundtland Commission it is much more important

to reduce the amount of waste generated. This will reduce the volume that otherwise must be treated or disposed of. This is first and foremost a problem of industrialized countries. But it is also a problem in NICs [newly industrializing countries] and developing countries, where the same severe problems are expected.

Waste transport is a growing problem.

Between 1982 and 1983, wastes transported within Western Europe for disposal in another country virtually doubled. For example, about 4,000 shipments of hazardous wastes went from the Netherlands to the German Democratic Republic in 1984. And the Federal Republic of Germany sent about 20,000 shipments to the German Democratic Republic the preceding year.

Industrial Pollution

Though many industries, particularly in the industrialized countries, have taken measures to diminish the most serious forms of pollution, the Brundtland Commission observes that the effects are only limited:

Taking the world as a whole, fertilizer run-off and sewage discharges into rivers, lakes, and coastal waters have increased, with resulting impacts on fishing, drinking-water supplies, and scenic beauty. The water quality of most major rivers has not markedly improved over the years. It is, in fact, worsening in many of them, as it is in many smaller rivers. Industrialized countries still suffer from 'traditional' forms of air and land pollution. Levels of sulphur and nitrogen oxides, suspended particulates, and hydrocarbons remain high and in some cases have increased. Air pollution in parts of many Third World countries has risen to levels worse than anything witnessed in the industrial countries during the 1960s.

In a recent report, the World Health Organization (WHO) concluded that approximately 600 million people live in areas where sulphur dioxide forms a health problem. One billion people are exposed to hazardous levels of suspended particles resulting from the combustion of coal, oil or wood.

Water pollution in a lake near Punmenend, Netherlands. (Marco Bakker/Hollandco Hoogte)

The Brundtland Commission is optimistic about possible measures.

At the beginning of the 1970s, both governments and industry were deeply worried about the costs of proposed environmental measures. Some felt that they would depress investment, growth, jobs, competitiveness, and trade, while driving up inflation. Such fears proved misplaced. A 1984 survey by the Organization for Economic Co-operation and Development (OECD), of assessments undertaken in a number of industrialized countries, concluded that expenditures on environmental measures over the past two decades had a positive effect on growth and employment as the increased demand they generated raised the output of economies operating at less than full capacity. In other words, a wastewater purification plant also is a product. If society wishes to, and can, purchase such products, it increases output. Purification technology represents a growth market. The benefits, including health, property and ecosystem damage avoided, have been significant. More important, these benefits have generally exceeded costs.

The Hole in the Ozone Layer

From 24 to 40 kilometres above the Earth's surface lies the ozone layer. Though ozone is present only in low concentrations, this layer forms an indispensable protective shield, preventing ultraviolet radiation from reaching the Earth. Scientists have recently discovered that the thickness of this layer is rapidly decreasing. 'Holes' are even being torn in the shield, through which the hazardous radiation can pass freely to Earth. The cause is air pollution.

The Poles

The holes in the ozone layer were first identified above the poles, particularly over the South Pole. The specific conditions occurring in these regions each winter render the ozone layer susceptible to attack by chlorofluorocarbons (CFCs). As mentioned earlier, these CFCs are commonly used as propellants in aerosols, as refrigerants in fridges, in the manufacture of polystyrene foam and for cleaning electronic print boards. They are ➡

⇨

special in that they react with hardly any other substance. Once they enter the atmosphere, they remain there for at least 70 to 120 years, rising very slowly until, at about a height of 30 kilometres, they come into contact with ultraviolet radiation. This causes them to decompose, releasing chlorine, which subsequently reacts with the ozone present at these heights. The ozone is decomposed and a thinning of the ozone layer occurs. This process is particularly vigorous above very cold regions.

Depletion of the ozone layer is currently taking place at a rate of several per cent a year. This process is also occurring above Europe. A 1988 study showed that in a single winter the ozone layer above the greater part of Europe, North America and the Soviet Union is reduced by more than 4.7 per cent.

The Effects

In the Dutch periodical *Natuur en Milieu* (February 1987), Lucas Reijnders describes the possible consequences of ozone depletion.

Owing to the decrease in the amount of ozone present in the ozone layer, more ultraviolet radiation is reaching the Earth's surface. This has substantial effects. Each one per cent reduction of the ozone layer increases the risk of skin cancer in white-skinned people by four per cent, and the risk of eye problems (such as cataracts) by 0.2 to 0.6 per cent. Skin infections, too, will increase. Certain plants will exhibit reduced growth, and aquatic animals in shallow water will see their lifespan diminished. The intense depletion of the ozone layer around the South Pole will, in all probability, have adverse effects on organisms living for shorter or longer periods near the surface in the oceans of Antarctica, such as krill and certain fish larvae. Krill is a generic name for a type of plankton consisting mainly of small crustaceans. It fulfils a key role in the ecosystem, serving as a staple diet for octopuses and fish and, together with these, for penguins and other sea birds, seals and whales.

➡

Scientists estimate that, if current trends continue, within a few years a loss of 10 per cent of the ozone layer should be reckoned with. In the United States alone, this would lead to 300,000 new cases of skin cancer each year.

Montreal

In 1987 the major industrialized countries signed a treaty in Montreal, Canada, in which they agreed that CFC production must no longer increase. It was further decided to halve production by the year 2000. Because of the many exceptions made, particularly for Third World countries, the reduction actually achieved in 2000 will not exceed 35 per cent. The problem is that CFCs have a long life in the atmosphere and take several years to rise to the ozone layer. Even if CFC production is cut back by more than one third, therefore, CFC concentrations will treble in the coming years. If production of these gases were stopped today, the ozone hole would continue to exist for at least another hundred years. In view of this, environmental organizations argue that CFC production should be decreased by at least 85 per cent, if not banned completely.

Measures

In most cases there are good substitutes for CFCs. In the United States and in the Scandinavian countries, CFCs in aerosols have been replaced by other, less objectionable substances, such as dimethyl ether and hydrocarbons. The Netherlands, too, under pressure from environmental and consumer organizations, has restricted the use of CFCs in aerosols. Water-based substitutes exist for cleaning electronic print boards. CFCs for refrigerators, air conditioning units and freezers present somewhat more of a problem. This category is suitable for re-use, but this would require the

⇨

organized collection of old refrigerators. Though it will be somewhat more expensive, here, too, substitutes for CFCs are available. CFCs are furthermore used in the manufacture of styrene plastics. The white, plastic foam used for the packaging of electrical equipment, cut meat and eggs and for the beakers in fast food restaurants are all produced using CFCs. It appears to be impossible to find safe alternatives for all these applications.

Action

In the spring of 1989 a further series of high level meetings was organized on the issue of ozone depletion. The latest of these, taking place in Helsinki, Finland, concluded that stronger measures should be taken than had been decided on in Montreal two years earlier. First of all, the Montreal Protocol should be implemented with a 100 per cent worldwide participation. Secondly, *all* CFCs should be phased out by the year 2000. Finally, two other gases, also damaging to the ozone layer — carbon tetrachloride and methyl chloroform — should be phased out by the same target date.

But even then, the levels of CFCs will not return to the (already high) 1985 levels before the end of the next century. Environmental organizations demand more radical measures. All gases likely to deplete ozone should be forbidden; likewise, so-called 'ozone friendly' gases, like HCFC 22, which are being promoted by the refrigeration industry. Recycling of such damaging gases should have priority.

The most serious prognosis for ozone layer depletion can be prevented. Nevertheless, governments and industry are not prepared to take fast enough action, for every change in production processes will cost them money. It is up to environmental and consumer organizations, but also individual citizens, to change this grave state of affairs.   ■

Accidents

In the three years of the Brundtland Commission's functioning, a series of serious industrial accidents took place.

> In 1984, liquid gas storage tanks exploded in Mexico City, killing 1,000 people and leaving thousands more homeless. Only months after the Bhopal tragedy in India, which killed over 3,000 people and injured 200,000 more, an accident at a plant in West Virginia in the United States operated by the parent company of the Bhopal facility resulted in emergency evacuation of residents and some health problems. In early November 1986, a fire at a warehouse of a chemicals manufacturer in Basel, Switzerland, sent toxic fumes into France and the Federal Republic of Germany, and released toxic chemicals into the Rhine, causing massive fish kills and affecting the water supply in countries downstream, all the way to the Netherlands.

Investigations in the United States have revealed that in the last 25 years there have occurred 17 major chemical accidents involving the release of greater quantities of toxic chemicals than in Bhopal. In 12 of these, chemicals more poisonous than the methyl isocyanate at Bhopal were released into the atmosphere. In addition to these accidents, between 1982 and 1988, 11,048 'incidents' in US factories were reported, an average of almost four a day!

The Brundtland Commission recommends a series of measures:

● 'Survey hazardous industrial operations and enforce regulations on safe operation;

● 'Create possibilities to locate polluting or hazardous facilities away from population centres;

● 'Provide plant workers with full information about the products and technologies they handle, and give them adequate training in safe operational procedures and emergency preparedness.

● 'Involve local governments and community residents in major siting decisions and emergency preparedness planning.'

Is This Progress?

In a reaction to the Brundtland Report, the Environmental Liaison

Centre, an international environmental and development organization established in Nairobi, Kenya, poses the question whether industrial growth is necessary and desirable. There are few within environmental and Third World organizations who would subscribe to a policy calling for economic growth involving a five- to tenfold increase in industrial output. Is the philosophy of the Brundtland Commission ('Industry is urged to do more with less') an acceptable one? Do we have to produce more? And can we afford to? In the eyes of many, it would be better for us to reduce industrial production by cutting back consumption and make haste with implementing drastic cuts in energy use.

Ecological objections to industrialization apart, environmental and Third World organizations consider any attempt by Third World countries to follow the industrial development pattern of the Western world to be unrealistic. It is true that multinational corporations increasingly locate parts (often the most environmentally hazardous parts) of their production processes in Third World countries, but the benefits for these countries — and certainly for the poorest parts of their population — will always be limited. They have hardly any influence on these internationally organized companies. At the same time, the multinationals will not allow any autonomous industrial growth in the Third World.

(6) Urbanization

> By the turn of the century, almost half the world will live in urban areas — from small towns to huge megacities. In the 21st century the world will for the greater part be urbanized. Over only 65 years, the developing world's urban population increased tenfold, from around 100 million in 1920 to close to one billion now. In 1940, only about one person in 100 lived in a city with a million or more inhabitants. By 1980, one in 10 people was a 'million city' resident.

Within ten years, Third World cities will have to house an additional three-quarters to one billion people. This means that they will need to step up their efforts by 15 per cent in order to provide the same services in terms of public transport, drinking water, sewerage systems and accommodation as they do now.

Causes

Why do millions of people move to cities that are becoming so crowded

Slum dwellers of Cartagena, Colombia, looking for useful refuse.
(Heinemann/Present)

Rural migrants build themselves a home from waste material in Nairobi,
Kenya. (Herzog/Present)

that living there seems well-nigh impossible?

To provide some insight into this complex problem, a distinction is often made between forces 'pulling' and forces 'pushing' people to the cities. The Brundtland Commission points to the 'pull' exerted by cities.

> Investments supported by governments and aid agencies have followed the same centralizing logic as private investments. Transportation facilities, educational and health institutions, and urban infrastructure and services were concentrated in the big cities. Rural–urban migration has followed the same pattern. A major reason why so many migrants in recent decades went to cities such as Nairobi, Manila, Lagos, Mexico City, Sao Paulo, Rangoon, or Port au Prince was the dominant role each centre came to play in its national economy.

In almost all countries there has been a huge flow of capital investment into the cities, at the expense of rural areas. The cities have also gained a certain attractiveness, with their neon advertisements and luxury products, and with their government offices, factories and universities. If one ever wants to become 'upwardly mobile', one must live in the city. In rural areas one remains 'backward' and grows isolated. That those daring enough to make the move to the city often have to live there in the most horrendous conditions does little to detract from this attraction.

More important than the attraction of the big city is the 'push' of rural living conditions. Farmers receive very low prices for their products, and in many cases most of the land, and the best land at that, is owned by big agricultural companies, operating on a commercial basis. For simple peasant families, forced to move to less productive soil, it is hardly possible to earn a living. The result is often erosion, water shortage, deforestation and other environmental problems, forcing the poorest to flee the rural areas altogether.

Besides urbanization, in the last few years the population growth in the cities themselves has been a major cause of the spread of shantytowns in many Third World countries.

Shantytowns

Hardboard, plastic, cardboard, corrugated iron, clothes and wood are the main 'building' materials of the shantytowns in many Third World cities. At night there are thousands of small fires, around which women crouch to cook their food. Large numbers of children, chickens, goats and pigs roam the 'streets'. The poor hygiene defies description. There are usually no sewers, no water, no toilets, no electricity, and when it rains the 'streets' turn into pools of mud. Infant mortality is very high, and almost everyone suffers from worms and infectious diseases. Although most of the people living in shantytowns do have work, it is not a registered, formal job. These are hardly to be found.

With few jobs available in the formal sector of the economy or government services, people have to find or create their own sources of income. These efforts have resulted in the rapid growth of what has been termed the 'informal sector', which provides much of the cheap goods and services essential to the city economies, business, and consumers. Without this market — visible on every street corner, but invisible in official economic statistics — many Third World countries would not be able to function.

Most of the so-called unemployed are in fact working 10–15 hours a day, six to seven days a week. They make money as small furniture makers or as tailors, by illegally distilling liquor, selling lottery tickets or shining shoes. Almost all members of the family contribute some money. 'Their problem is not so much underemployment as underpayment,' in the words of the Brundtland Commission.

Examples of Rapid Population Growth in Third World Countries

City	1950	Population (in millions)	United Nations Predictions for Year 2000
Mexico City	3.05	16.0 (1982)	26.3
Sao Paulo	2.7	12.6 (1980)	24.0
Bombay	3.0	8.2 (1981)	16.0
Djakarta	1.45	6.2 (1977)	12.8
Cairo	2.5	8.5 (1979)	13.2
Delhi	1.4 (1951)	5.8 (1981)	13.3
Manila	1.78	5.5 (1980)	11.1
Lagos	0.27 (1952)	4.0 (1980)	8.3
Bogota	0.61	3.9 (1985)	9.6
Nairobi	0.14	0.83 (1979)	5.3
Dar es Salaam	0.15 (1960)	0.90 (1981)	4.6
Khartoum	0.18	1.05 (1978)	4.1
Amman	0.03	0.78 (1978)	1.5
Nouakchott	0.006	0.25 (1982)	1.1
Manaus	0.11	0.51 (1980)	1.1
Santa Cruz	0.059	0.26 (1976)	1.0

Most recent censuses, if available, otherwise, estimates.

Measures to Be Taken

According to the Brundtland Commission, measures must be taken to curb the flow of people to the cities. One way to achieve this is to make cities less attractive by decreasing food subsidies and reducing the concentration of energy supplies and services in the cities. The Brundtland Commission advocates the growth of secondary regional centres. According to the Commission, such a policy has advantages because these centres may build on the economic advantages of their regions and play an important role in, for instance, trade and decentralized provision of government services. With these secondary economic centres, urban development may stimulate agricultural growth, because business can respond directly to the local products that are available.

A Viable Solution for the Cities Themselves

It is important to check the growth of cities. However, it is doubtful whether the policy suggested by the Brundtland Commission will accomplish this. Reinforcement of local trade and urbanization of rural areas will benefit, above all, the wealthier sections of the population. In the opinion of many experts, if farmers are to have a future, they will have to be given (back) land. Land reforms are thus the main policy instrument called for. However, such reforms have not yet been implemented, and the cities continue to grow. This calls for measures adapted to the reality that will be facing us soon.

The cities will have to cope with the population explosion. In this respect, a major contribution can be made by local authorities such as municipal councils and community services.

> A strong local government can ensure that the needs, customs, urban forms, social priorities, and environmental conditions of the local area are reflected in local plans for urban development. But local authorities have not been given the political power, decision-making capacity and access to revenues needed to carry out their functions.

So states the Commission.

The manner in which urban development is carried out is decisive for its effectiveness. An example serves to illustrate how a sum of $20 million may reach only 12,000 people, when it could reach 600,000.

Three Ways to Use $20 Million to Improve Conditions in a City of One Million People

Option 1:

Build 2,000 public housing units for poor families (with an average of six family members), each costing $10,000. Conditions are improved for 12,000 people, but few poor families can be expected to be able to repay the costs involved. If the city's population grows at 5 per cent annually, 630,000 new inhabitants will be added over 10 years, so only a tiny fraction of the total population will have benefited.

Option 2:

Establish a 'site-and-service scheme', whereby poor families are themselves responsible for building their houses on an allocated site supplied with piped water, connection to a sewer system, and electricity, roads, and drainage. At $2,000 per plot, this means housing for some 60,000 people — about 10 per cent of merely this city's population growth over 10 years.

Option 3:

Allocate $100,000 to a neighbourhood organization representing 1,000 poor households (6,000 people) in an existing low-income settlement. It chooses to improve drainage and roads, build a health clinic, establish a co-operative to produce inexpensive building materials and components, and reblock the settlement to improve access roads and provide 50 new plots. With $10 million, 100 such community initiatives are supported, reaching 600,000 people and providing 5,000 new housing plots. Many new jobs are created. The remaining $10 million is spent on installing piped water; at $100 per household, all 600,000 people are reached.

The suggestion made by the Brundtland Commission is clear. The example shows how important it is to involve the people in the projects. The Brundtland Commission also draws attention to the way houses are built. Without involving the community, and particularly the women, housing projects run a great risk of ending in failure.

Attention to Women's Requirements in Housing Projects

Project developers often design blocks of houses and roads without taking into account the important role of women in and near the house in most Third World shantytowns. House designs and plot sizes rarely consider the fact that many women will want to use their houses as workshops (to make clothes, for instance) or as shops, which in fact are often forbidden in low-income housing projects. Application procedures for low-income housing sometimes require 'husbands' to apply; this excludes women-headed households — between 30 and 50 per cent of all households. Women's special needs in different cultures are ignored. In Islamic societies, for example, women's need for private open space within the house is rarely considered in house designs, while their need for relatively sheltered pathways to get to shops and clinics is hardly ever acknowledged in site layouts. ∎

Recommendations

The Brundtland Commission's strategy is summarized in a number of recommendations:

● 'Provide legal tenure to those living in "illegal" settlements, with basic services provided by public authorities;

● 'Ensure that the land and other resources people need to build or improve their housing are available;

● 'Supply existing and new housing areas with infrastructure for roads, sewers and water;

● 'Set up neighbourhood offices to provide advice and technical assistance on how housing can be built better and cheaper, and on how health and hygiene can be improved;

● 'Plan and guide the city's physical expansion to anticipate and encompass land needed for new housing, agricultural land, parks, and children's play areas;

● 'Consider how public intervention could improve conditions for tenants and those living in cheap rooming or boarding houses;

● 'Change housing finance systems to make cheap loans available to lower-income and community groups.'

4. Managing the Commons

The greater part of the world around us falls outside national borders. Who can own the air, the oceans, space? Those areas not delineated by national borders form our 'Global Commons'.

International conventions have been drawn up for some of these Global Commons. Officially, there are three: the oceans outside national territorial waters, Antarctica, and outer space. It has been proposed to add other regions, such as the atmosphere, which is also shared by all people alike. With air pollution being no respecter of national boundaries, this is being increasingly appreciated. Conservationists argue that tropical rain forests, too, should be placed under common management.

1. The Oceans

Covering over 70 per cent of the Earth's surface, oceans play a critical role in maintaining its life-support systems, in moderating its climate, and in sustaining animals and plants, including minute, oxygen-producing phytoplankton. They provide protein, transportation, energy, employment, recreation, and other economic, social and cultural activities. The oceans also provide the ultimate sink for the by-products of human activities. Huge, closed septic tanks, they receive wastes from cities, farms and industries via sewage outfalls, dumping from barges and ships, coastal run-off, river discharge, and even atmospheric transport.

So says the Brundtland Report.

Fisheries

Overfishing has become an urgent problem: 'World fisheries have been expanding since the Second World War, with the global catch rising at a steady 6–7 per cent annually, from 20 million to 65 million tonnes between 1950 and 1969. But after 1970, as more and more stocks were depleted, the average annual growth in catches fell to only about 1 per cent.' The Brundtland Commission quotes the United Nations Food and Agriculture Organization, which sees only limited scope for further growth. Current catches, amounting to 80 million tonnes, should not rise above 100 million tonnes. As food demand is set to increase further, this is not an optimistic forecast. This problem was one of the factors leading to expansion of the so-called Exclusive Economic Zones, territorial waters as distinct from international waters, which give countries some degree of control over catches in their coastal waters.

The Exclusive Economic Zones are included in the Law of the Sea Convention, which in 1987 had been signed by 159 countries, though ratified by only 32. Ratification is necessary to give this global convention legal validity. Resistance has come from the industrialized countries in particular. The Law of the Sea reduces the high seas by some 35 per cent, a zone of 200 nautical miles (370 kilometres) from the coast being declared part of the coastal state. The Law of the Sea also provides for the regulation of seabed mining, another matter that is hard to swallow for industrialized countries. They reject any controls, for they are the ones to profit most by the current situation, and it is not in their economic interest to change it.

Especially for developing countries, which do not have large ships with sophisticated equipment, an Exclusive Economic Zone is a matter of survival. A parallel can again be drawn with agriculture. Commercial fisheries, often for exports and carried out by foreign companies, threaten the protein supply of the people in the coastal areas of Third World countries.

Marine Waste Disposal

The dumping of radioactive waste in the world's oceans has hit the national and international headlines many times. Blockades by activists and by Greenpeace ships, which often gave the dumping vessels a hard time, stirred up a lively discussion. In 1983 a temporary (voluntary) halt to sea dumping of low-level radioactive waste was agreed upon by the London Dumping Convention. With the International Maritime Organization (IMO) acting as secretariat, the 61 contracting parties to this convention regularly discuss sea

A grebe has fallen victim to oil pollution on the North Sea coast. (Michiel Wijnbergh)

dumping. Following the stands taken by the London Dumping Convention in 1983 and 1985, sea dumping of radioactive waste was halted, pending studies on the environmental risks of this practice. Before that period, the industrialized countries had already dumped more than 90,000 tonnes of radioactive waste in the oceans.

Measures Needed

The threats to the oceans are innumerable.

> The amount of oil spilled annually from tankers now approaches 1.5 million tonnes. The larger part, 1.1 million tonnes, involves deliberate discharges. The rapid depletion of the ozone layer and the consequent increase in ultraviolet radiation poses a threat not only to human health but to ocean life. Some scientists believe that this radiation could kill sensitive phytoplankton and fish larvae floating near the ocean's surface, damaging ocean food chains and possibly disrupting planetary support systems.

The Brundtland Commission proposes several measures to achieve sustainable management of the oceans as soon as possible:

- Strengthen the capacity for national action, especially in developing countries;

- Improve fisheries management;

- Reinforce co-operation in areas with semi-enclosed and regional seas;

- Strengthen controls over ocean disposal of hazardous and nuclear wastes;

- Make the provisions of the Law of the Sea tougher.

2. Space

Though outer space may seem infinitely large, for earth dwellers it is certainly not. Increasingly, space users are meeting one another, particularly in a band of space 36,000 kilometres above the equator.

Most communication and military satellites are in this so-called geosynchronous orbit. Since signals from the satellites interfere with one another, the space available in this orbit is limited. It can accommodate at most 180 satellites.

Space Pollution

Rockets and satellites leave all sorts of debris in space: empty fuel tanks, motor components, satellites that are no longer working. This space waste accumulates in a band between 160 and 1,760 kilometres above the Earth's surface. The Brundtland Commission also draws attention to the risk of military activities in space (a case in point is 'Star Wars'): 'The most important measure to minimize space debris, therefore, is to prevent the further testing and deployment of space weapons.'

Many spacecraft are nuclear-powered. Once their mission is completed, they may fall back to Earth and cause nuclear contamination, especially if large components reach the Earth's surface. The Brundtland Commission proposes a complete ban on the use of nuclear energy in space, except for very long-range expeditions, for instance to Mars or further.

A Space Regime

The Brundtland Commission advocates that rules for the use of outer space be drawn up to ensure 'that the activities of a few do not undermine the possibilities of use of this resource for all.' The first step towards space management has been taken by dividing the geosynchronous band. This would need to be extended to encompass a ban on the use of nuclear materials in space.

3. Antarctica

The Antarctic continent — larger than the United States and Mexico combined — for over a generation has been managed under a regime of multilateral co-operation that has secured environmental protection. Signed on 1 December 1959, the Antarctica Treaty has been the vehicle for a number of important initiatives in pursuit of its two primary objectives:

to maintain Antarctica for peaceful uses only, prohibiting all military activities, nuclear explosions, and disposal of radioactive wastes; and to promote freedom of scientific investigation in Antarctica and international co-operation to that end.

Challenges

The bitterly cold South Pole region is under threat. As the Brundtland Commission states:

> Under the combined pressures of economic, technological, environmental and other trends, there are new initiatives to establish a regime for minerals exploitation. New questions about equitable management are presenting challenges that may reshape the political context of the continent within the next decade.

Antarctica may be a cold, inhospitable region, but it contains mineral resources — both metals and oil. As these become scarcer in the rest of the world, and as technology progresses, the potential for exploiting these minerals is becoming ever greater. But who will control them, who will sell them?

At present, responsibility is shouldered by eighteen countries, each of which has a claim on the continent. To be eligible for joining this group, prospective members are expected to exhibit a real interest in the region by funding a great deal of research. Some countries are not in a position to do so, and this can give rise to bitterness. A more serious problem is that at least seven countries claim parts of Antarctica as their sovereign territory. Third World countries blame the industrialized world for setting up a management regime that excludes them from future exploitation of the resources hidden under the thick Antarctic ice.

Environmental Disaster

Though still on the drawing board, exploitation of resources is already threatening the sensitive environment of the South Pole region. On its own, the waste left behind by research groups amounts to many thousands of tonnes. At the end of 1988, the French started work on a new air strip at their Antarctic base. Using dynamite and heavy machinery, they destroyed the breeding grounds of thousands of birds, in blatant violation of the Antarctica Treaty.

Steel works seen from refuse tip at Spaarnwoude, Netherlands. (Michiel Wijnbergh)

The presence of these research groups is not inspired solely by science. The more research conducted, the stronger the claim the researching country has on Antarctica. According to the Brundtland Commission, 'the 18 Consultative Parties are conducting negotiations among themselves to complete an agreed legal framework for determining the environmental acceptability of possible minerals exploration and development in Antarctica and to govern any such activities.' Because of the extreme cold, the continent is exceedingly vulnerable to environmental pollution. Over the millennia, the food chains have developed so as to ensure that not a milligram of food is lost, for food is energy and energy is heat! When pollutants enter this food chain, it spells certain death for large numbers of animals. This was again confirmed in early 1989, when an Argentine ship sank near Antarctica, spilling its oil into the sea.

For all these reasons, environmental organizations eye current developments with suspicion; they would prefer Antarctica to remain unspoiled and to see all exploitation of minerals banned.

Recommendations

The Brundtland Commission makes some cautious recommendations. It believes that co-operation between scientists should be strengthened. More countries should be involved in the management of Antarctica. Furthermore, the member states of the Antarctica Treaty should 'foster dialogue among politicians, scientists, environmentalists, and industries.'

'It is important that minerals activity takes place only in consonance with a regime that guarantees implementation of the most stringent standards needed to protect the continent's environment and share the proceeds equitably.' The Brundtland Commission was not prepared to go so far as to exclude completely the recovery of minerals from Antarctica.

4. The Atmosphere and the Rain Forests

Laws always lag behind actual developments, and this holds even more strongly for international agreements. This explains why the air around us, the atmosphere, has not been declared one of the Global Commons. The atmosphere can be viewed as a kind of planetary heritage. 'Who can own the air?' the Indian chief Seattle asked. He predicted disaster if we continue to lay waste to our environment.

Who Can Own The Air?

The following is an extract from a declaration made in 1885 by Seattle, chief of the Duwamish tribes, to an audience of American government representatives who had come to buy the Indian land:

> The air is precious to the Red Man, for every being shares the same air — animals, trees, people, all partake of the same air. The White Man does not care about the air he breathes. Like a man who has been dying for many days, he is insensitive to evil vapours.
>
> But if we are to sell our land to you, you must remember that to us the air is valuable, that the air communicates its breath to all the life it sustains. The wind that gave my grandfather his first breath also receives his last. And the wind must also breathe the spirit of life into our children.

Seattle has been proven right. It is the wind that, with ever greater frequency, brings death. Death to fish and trees in the form of acid rain. Death to children and adults alike, in the form of radioactivity. Nation-states think they have found a solution: they have kept on increasing the height of their smoke-stacks so as to export the pollution. It would be a good thing if the atmosphere were considered a common heritage, belonging to all humanity, for it would mean that governments and industries would have to account for the wastes they emit to it. Perhaps this is the reason why an international treaty to this end is not even on the agenda.

Neither have the tropical rain forests yet been declared a common resource. Conservationists advocate that the world's major rain forests be given international status. As is the case for Antarctica, an international commission should be established for their management. The expression 'international heritage' is often used to indicate that these areas are so important to us all, and to future generations, that it is imperative that they be preserved for ever. Those who propose making the rain forests international 'property' believe that national governments cannot guarantee their preservation. In their opinion, this can only be achieved through effective international control.

5. Peace, Security, Development and the Environment

'Among the dangers facing the environment, the possibility of nuclear war is undoubtedly the gravest. Environmental stress is both a cause and an effect of political tension and military conflict,' the Brundtland Report states. 'Nations have often fought to assert or resist control over raw materials, energy supplies, land, river basins, sea passages, and other key environmental resources. Such conflicts are likely to increase as these resources become scarcer and competition for them increases.'

Environmental Problems as a Source of Conflict

Poverty, injustice, environmental degradation and armed conflict interact in complex and potent ways. In recent years, this is becoming more manifest as we see the emergence of 'environmental refugees'.

The immediate cause of any mass movement of refugees may appear to be political upheaval and military violence. But the underlying causes often include the deterioration of the natural resource base and its capacity to support the population.

Wars have always compelled people to leave their homes and their lands, to become refugees. They still do. But in addition, we now have the phenomenon of environmental refugees. In 1984–85 some 10 million Africans fled their homes, accounting for two-thirds of all refugees worldwide. Their flight was not surprising in a region where 35 million suffered from famine. Many of them swarmed into cities. But many others moved across national boundaries, heightening inter-state tensions. The Ivory Coast, for instance, which depends for much of its revenues on timber, is suffering rapid deforestation. Agriculture destroys 4.5 times as much forest land in the Ivory Coast as logging does, and one-third of landless people are immigrants.

The Brundtland Report provides more examples. The people fleeing Haiti are moving out of a country suffering the world's most severe erosion. Here, farmers can no longer earn a living. El Salvador, one of the most unstable nations of Central America, also has some of the worst erosion rates in the region.

South Africa's apartheid regime has designed a so-called homelands policy for its black population. These homelands, covering 14 per cent of South Africa's territory, are to accommodate 72 per cent of the population. These overcrowded lands, which have rapidly lost their productivity, cannot cope with such a population concentration. Young blacks see themselves forced to flee the homelands, only to become dirt cheap labour, virtually without rights, for white employers. The homelands policy has also severely degraded the soil in many parts of the country.

Raw Materials

It was the quest for raw materials that underlay much of the competition between the European powers for colonies in the Third World where they could exploit the population. Modern conflicts in the Middle East inevitably contain the seeds of great power intervention, in part because of their interests in securing oil supplies.

According to the Brundtland Commission, the exploitation of raw materials has always been an excuse for oppression. It was not because of their headdress that many millions of Indians in South and North America were killed. It was because the white man needed their mineral-rich land, their forests and their agricultural produce.

People are still being killed for raw materials. Today, the process is usually more subtle, however. Though the Brundtland Report does not discuss the massive political repression under the world's dictatorships, clearly the West's prosperity and the related large-scale consumption of raw materials (with the associated environmental degradation) has much to do with these regimes. Whether it be copper from Chile, bananas from Guatemala, or uranium from Namibia, political suppression is the order of the day in many, many countries producing raw materials important to the industrialized world. In every case, care for the environment has been subordinated to production. Exploitation of raw materials, degradation of the environment and violation of human rights frequently go hand in hand.

Sizewell Nuclear Power Station, Suffolk, Sizewell 'A' in foreground and Sizewell 'B' site to right. November 1989. (Philip Carr/Environmental Picture Library)

Uranium Scandal in Niger

In the mines of Niger, which are under French control, workers are provided with hardly any protection against inhalation of radioactive radon gas. Boys aged fifteen and sixteen are irradiated. Almost to a man, the workers are Tuareg nomads, and they are given absolutely no information on the effects of the mining operations. Radiation levels are not checked, neither is there is any health supervision.

These are just some of the facts revealed by a British TV producer after a visit with a camera team to the Arlit uranium mine in the north of this Sahel country Niger. They were the first outsiders to visit the mine. Christopher Olgiati is a long, slender man. He does not have anything against Niger's military regime; he even defends the government against widely voiced accusations that it allowed Libya to steal uranium ore. According to his information, this is a rumour spread by the CIA.

Chris Olgiati might have been a proponent of nuclear energy. In short, he could not be accused of holding any prejudice against uranium mining. Nevertheless, he returned deeply shocked from a ten-day visit to one of the world's major sources of uranium. The working conditions of the miners are unbelievable. The contrast between their living conditions and those of the French management could not be greater.

'Arlit is in the middle of nowhere,' he says. 'It's an artificial oasis, built entirely in colonial style. It has its own dormitory town, complete with supermarkets, horse races and luxury articles flown in from France. The cultural clash with the nomadic labourers is inconceivable.'

According to Olgiati, the workers come to the mine of their own accord; there is no need for forced recruitment. The nomads often stay no longer than a week, take their pay and disappear into the desert. In some cases they leave after only a day. 'It was a major complaint of the French,' Olgiati says. 'The workers just

➡

keep on walking off.' The French tell the indigenous people nothing about the fact that they are working in the most hazardous form of mining in the world. There are no checks on the radiation doses to which the workers are exposed and there is no health care whatsoever. Many of the workers will probably contract cancer. 'A friendly French manager in Arlit told us they have absolutely no idea what is going to happen to these people in the next twenty or thirty years.'

The TV team also visited the large underground mine. 'One day spent underground was enough,' Olgiati relates. 'Air conditioning seemed to be adequate, but the noise of the drilling operations was deafening. And I did not see anyone wearing protective masks or earplugs. At the end of the day the miners emerged from the mine shafts with their bodies covered with thick layers of radioactive dust.'

Arlit is not the only uranium mine in Niger, but it is the oldest and still one of the largest. Commercial production started in 1971. First, the best uranium ore was extracted, ore with concentrations of up to three per cent. The average concentration has now dropped to a quarter of a per cent. This means that at least 400 kilograms of ore-bearing rock must be processed to obtain one kilogram of concentrated uranium. From mines in the United States, operated by companies like Kerr McGee, it is known that many miners die of cancer — and these mines were probably cleaner than those at Arlit. The French have in effect condemned thousands of Niger's inhabitants to death.

The mine's management is firmly in the hands of the French, though Niger's government holds a one-third interest. 'It felt like I was at a war front,' Olgiati says. 'Arlit is very important to the French. There is a giant transmitter for direct communication with France. They were not at all pleased with the presence of a British TV team.'

Niger's uranium is not only important for France's aggressive nuclear energy programme, but also for the production of nuclear arms. Colonel Gadafy of Libya, who would like nothing better than to be a nuclear

⇨

negotiator representing the Islamic world, also has interests. Niger has exported hundreds of tonnes of uranium to Libya, but both Niger and France are still very much afraid that Gadafy will one day take over the Arlit mine by force.

The most acute danger, however, stems from the mine itself. As in many uranium mines, the poorest people in the world are working here in some of the most deadly surroundings imaginable. And they must do this in order to produce raw materials to power everything from electric heaters to model trains in the richest countries of the world. The miners themselves are unaware of the effects of the work on their health. And no one in the West, and certainly not in France, will ever know how they suffer.

Source: 'Keep it in the Ground', 1982. Based on an article by Roger Moody.

■

Nuclear Energy and Nuclear Weapons

For development, energy is required. Increasingly, nuclear power is being employed as an energy source in both industrial and developing countries. In discussing the energy problem, mention was made of the environmental hazards of nuclear power. The Brundtland Commission is very cautious on this subject, although it did state that alternatives to nuclear energy should be developed and top priority assigned to energy conservation measures.

The Commission did not dwell on the relationship between nuclear weapons and nuclear power, however. Three of the key materials for nuclear weapons are uranium, plutonium and tritium, substances that are also used and produced in nuclear power stations. Plutonium does not occur in nature; it is made by man, in nuclear power plants. It is the most toxic substance in existence, lethal to humans in the minutest of quantities. Any country in possession of nuclear power stations and the associated technology can also possess nuclear weapons. The nuclear powers have already made use of this relationship for a long time. Hundreds of nuclear power stations in these countries produce material for mass destruction purposes. The same may happen in developing countries with nuclear power stations. India, for one, has developed nuclear weapons, while it is almost certain that Argentina, Brazil and Pakistan are running nuclear arms programmes. Attempts are being made to ensure that nuclear technology can be spread without enabling the recipient countries to produce nuclear weapons. Methods to achieve this include inspections in power stations and export bans on plutonium and the technologies required for nuclear weapons production. The International Atomic Energy Agency, a UN agency with its headquarters in Vienna, is responsible for these inspections. However, many critics doubt whether such inspections work in practice. Many countries refuse to co-operate and the Agency's small team of technicians cannot possibly handle all the work involved in inspecting hundreds of nuclear plants and other installations. And if a country has the technology and wants to use it for military purposes, ways can be found to do so secretly for, after all, a nuclear bomb need only contain five to ten kilos of plutonium or enriched uranium. Such amounts can now be produced in a small laboratory; with the right raw materials, even a student is able to build a simple nuclear weapon.

Conflict as a Cause of Environmental Degradation

Arms competition and armed conflict create major obstacles to sustainable development. They make huge claims on scarce material resources. They pre-empt human resources and wealth that could be used to combat the collapse of environmental support systems, the poverty, and the underdevelopment that in combination contribute so much to contemporary political insecurity.

Nuclear Weapons

'The likely consequences of nuclear war make other threats to the environment pale into insignificance. Nuclear weapons represent a qualitatively new step in the development of warfare.' In the view of the Brundtland Commission, the major effect of a nuclear war would be the ensuing 'nuclear winter'. 'The theory of nuclear winter contends that the smoke and dust ejected into the atmosphere by a nuclear war could absorb enough solar radiation to remain aloft for some time, preventing sunlight from reaching the surface of the Earth, causing a widespread and prolonged cooling of land areas.' Even if humankind could survive a nuclear war, it is highly questionable whether the effects would not spell a definitive end to our existence. 'A nuclear war cannot be won,' the Brundtland Commission concludes.

CND demonstration, London 1981. (M. Gilchrist/Environmental Picture Library)

Conventional War

Nuclear weapons may annihilate the world, but the effects of conventional weapons can be almost as destructive. War and military preparations have disastrous consequences for the environment: just consider the areas set aside for military manoeuvres, weapons testing, land claimed in anticipation of a possible war, etc.

Perhaps the peoples of the Pacific islands know best the effects of war and preparations for war on man's environment and on life itself. In the Second World War these peaceful islands were flooded with troops. Violence engulfed entire peoples. Bombing left some of the islands so bare of forest that planes had to be used to scatter grass seeds in order to stop erosion. For the island peoples of the Pacific, the Second World War was only one step in the escalation of violence they have witnessed. In the past they have been preyed upon by the scum of the seas, pirates, whalers and such like. After the War, many islands were converted into permanent military establishments. On Johnson Island, 30,000 tonnes of obsolete American chemical weapons have been stored. An incineration plant is presently under construction to 'destroy' these stocks, but the islanders no longer trust Western technologies.

However, the worst thing to confront the people of the Pacific Islands is the use of their islands as testing grounds for nuclear arms and guided missiles by France and the superpowers.

Vietnam

In the sixties, and particularly in the early seventies, American B-52 bombers dropped napalm, millions of bombs and toxic chemicals such as the notorious defoliant, Agent Orange, on war-stricken Vietnam. In its war with the United States, Vietnam lost more than 200 million hectares of tropical rain forest due to the use of bombs and toxic chemicals such as the notorious chemicals. Vast areas of land are still bare, incapable of natural recovery. Half of South Vietnam's mangrove forests were destroyed by chemical poisoning.

Destruction of forests leads to massive erosion. Huge quantities of fertile soil are washed from deforested mountain slopes into the sea. Erosion threatens more

➡

than 40 per cent of Vietnam's land area. In Quang Binh province almost 20,000 hectares of forest were destroyed between 1964 and 1968. Two years later, the number of floods in this area had almost trebled. The country is pitted with 25 million bomb craters, having an average diameter of 50 metres, spread over forests, mountains and rice fields. This alone means that an area covering 125,000 hectares has literally been blown into the sky! The craters form breeding places for disease-transmitting insects. Malaria has caused permanent damage to the health of millions of Vietnamese.

In spite of the war, Vietnam's population has grown fast. In the last forty years the population has doubled to 60 million. This means that, on average, there are 200 people living on each square kilometre. For Southeast Asia as a whole the figure is 75. In the year 2000, less than half a hectare will be available for each Vietnamese.

Professor Vo Quy, a biologist at Hanoi University, is not pessimistic. Vietnam has made a National Plan for environmental conservation. One of the major tasks of the government is to prevent environmental destruction due to economic growth. Use of pesticides in agriculture, for example, is increasing at an alarming rate. In 1959 total consumption stood at a minute 100 tonnes. Twenty years later, this had increased to 22,000 tonnes, applied to half of the land under cultivation. According to Professor Quy, in Hanoi 'millions of litres of dirty, polluted water, containing poison, bacteria and parasites, flow into lakes and rivers. This takes place within the city, in its suburbs, its slums.'

The government acknowledges these problems and has prepared plans to change the situation. Reforestation has been started. Each year, 120,000 hectares are reforested, with half of the trees surviving. Sixteen parks and nature reserves have been set up, and another seventy proposed. Families receive three to four hectares of land and are encouraged to plant trees. Saplings and fertilizer are made freely available, and the fuelwood may be sold. Schoolchildren are encouraged to plant two trees each year.

It remains to be seen whether this will really provide a solution to the environmental problems of Vietnam which, due to exploitation and thirty years of colonial war, is in deep trouble. Official figures show that, between 1985 and 1990, more than 15 million hectares of forest will have disappeared because of commercial tree felling operations. In the same period, the reforestation programme will provide only 300,000 hectares of new forest. For the environment, and for the people who depend on nature for their living, the war will continue for a long time to come.   ∎

The Costs of the 'Arms Culture'

'The absence of war is not peace.' At the end of his presidency, Eisenhower stated that each gun made, each naval ship launched, each missile fired, in the final analysis means that money is robbed from those who are hungry and unfed, and from those who are cold and unclothed. Brundtland put it this way:

> Global military spending in 1985 was well in excess of $900 billion. This was more than the total income of the poorest half of humanity. It represented the equivalent of almost $1,000 for every one of the world's 1 billion poorest. Three-quarters of this expenditure is in the industrialized world.
>
> The distorting effects of the 'arms culture' are most striking in the deployment of scientific personnel. Half a million scientists are employed on weapons research world-wide, and they account for around half of all research and development expenditure. This exceeds the total combined spending on developing new energy sources, improving human health, raising agricultural productivity, and controlling pollution. Military research and development — $70–80 billion world-wide in 1984 — is growing at twice the rate of military spending as a whole.

The arms trade has expanded enormously, as Brundtland makes clear: 'The export of arms has been valued at more than $35 billion annually. The arms trade is estimated to have absorbed over $300 billion over the last two decades, three-quarters in the form of sales to developing countries.' The arms trade has a destructive effect on the economies of both importing and exporting countries, for weapons produce only destruction. They have no inherent economic return. The billions of dollars invested in the arms trade are a form of capital destruction. The Brundtland Commission points out that this leads to increased dependence of Third World countries, arms purchases having to be financed by means of foreign exchange. 'It has been estimated that 20 per cent of the external debt acquired by non-oil developing countries could be attributed to arms imports.' In this respect, too, the arms trade has environmental consequences. Foreign currency does not simply flow into a country but must be earned — for instance, by the export of agricultural products, causing farmers to lose their land and move on to the vulnerable uplands, or by felling the rain forests and exporting the valuable wood.

Measure to Be Taken

It is not easy for an international group of experts to find cut-and-dried answers to problems relating to disarmament, development and environmental conservation. The reaction of the Brundtland Commission confirms this. It pleads for reinforcement of international agreements aimed at further disarmament. It also recommends installation of an early warning system for predicting and reporting major environmental disasters. This would enable prevention of such disasters and eliminate causes of conflicts.

Since the Brundtland Commission does not propose many concrete measures, it makes sense to take a look at statements by other groups of experts on the same problems. Back in 1981 the Secretary-General of the United Nations published a study highlighting the relation between armaments and development. The group of 27 experts responsible for this report drew up a long list of recommendations, some of which were directed at reconversion of the arms industry into a 'peace industry'. They argued that governments should create a climate enabling rapid reconversion of the arms industry. In part, this could be financed by economizing on arms purchases. The group further urged that all governments, but particularly those of the major military powers, should prepare estimates of the nature and magnitude of the short- and long-term economic and social costs attributable to their military preparations, so as to inform the public at large.

Information on military expenditures and the ensuing social costs should be made public. The Brazilian environmentalist Fernando Fernandes, in a reaction to the Brundtland Report, states that:

In fact, press freedom and well-informed NGOs are extremely important in avoiding plunging the planet into a spiral of environmental deterioration and military confrontation. It would be naive to believe that, without such freedom, governments of the leading countries would reach the agreements the world is waiting for.

6. Proposals for Action

If environmental destruction and underdevelopment are brought about by human hands, then we, as humans, can also contribute to a solution to these problems. The world, with all its living beings, is not a machine; it is an interdependent community. In our daily lives we accept a great deal of organization. We pay taxes, we conform to laws, we inform one another about everything under the sun. Still, so far, we have proved incapable of finding an adequate answer to the threats facing our biosphere, our very future. Yet this can change! In the preceding chapters many initiatives have already been suggested. Below, possible international actions, as proposed by the Brundtland Commission, are summarized.

Institutional and Legal Change

Sustainable development should be everyone's responsibility.

> Sustainable development objectives should be incorporated in the terms of reference of those cabinet and legislative committees dealing with national economic policy and planning as well as those dealing with key sectoral and international policies. As an extension of this, the major economic and sectoral agencies of governments should now be made directly responsible and fully accountable for ensuring that their policies, programmes, and budgets support development that is ecologically as well as economically sustainable.

This is one of the Brundtland Commission's most important conclusions. All ministries, all industries, all consultative bodies, all advisory committees are responsible for a sustainable future. Governments should prepare annual reports detailing the environmental changes taking place. The state of the environment should be presented together with traditional annual budgets and economic plans. 'All countries should develop a foreign policy for the environment. Such a policy needs to reflect the fact that the policies of a country have a growing impact on the environmental resource base of other nations and the commons (the oceans, Antarctica, outer space).'

The Brundtland Commission suggests that major international organizations, such as the Organization for Economic Co-operation and Development (OECD) and the United Nations, should assume a role in this respect.

Dealing with the Effects

Third World countries and industrialized countries are confronted with a broad range of environmental problems. Organizations for environmental protection should therefore be given extra support, particularly in the Third World. The Brundtland Commission specifically mentions the role of non-governmental organizations (NGOs), such as environmental groups and farmers' co-operatives, which in many cases are much more effective than official agencies in stimulating environmental recovery. The Commission recommends giving more (financial) support to them.

One of the organizations to which the Brundtland Commission assigns a critical role is the United Nations Environment Programme (UNEP). Established in 1972, UNEP was given the task of stimulating, coordinating and providing policy guidance on environmental activities within the United Nations. With a budget that has been reduced over the years from $100 million to $30 million, UNEP is not capable of meeting the increasing demands made on it. In the opinion of the Brundtland Commission this situation should change, with UNEP being given a central role in implementation of the global agenda for scientific research and technical development for environmental protection. Its environmental data collection and assessment functions (Earthwatch) should be strengthened, and UNEP should provide stronger support to NGOs.

The Global Risks

The Brundtland Commission recommends establishment of a Global Risk Assessment Programme, in which non-governmental groups should have majority participation. The aim of this programme is to identify the critical threats to survival and assess the causes and likely human, economic and ecological consequences of those threats. Reports should be published at regular intervals and be made available to the general public.

Non-Governmental Organizations

'Scientific groups and NGOs have played — with the help of young people — a major part in the environmental movement.' NGOs should give a high priority to the continuation of their present networking on development co-operation projects, while in many countries governments need to recognize and extend NGOs' right to know and access to information as well as their right to participate in decision-making, according to the Commission.

Legal Means

National and international law has traditionally lagged behind events. Today, legal regimes are being rapidly outdistanced by the accelerating pace and expanding scale of impacts on the environmental base of development. Human laws must be reformulated to keep human activities in harmony with the unchanging and universal laws of nature. There is an urgent need:

- to recognize and respect the reciprocal rights and responsibilities of individuals and states regarding sustainable development;

- to establish and apply new norms for state and inter-state behaviour to achieve sustainable development;

- to strengthen and extend the application of existing laws and international agreements in support of sustainable development;

- to reinforce existing methods and develop new procedures for avoiding and resolving environmental disputes.

In the view of the Brundtland Commission, it is time to draw up a Universal Declaration on Environmental Protection and Sustainable Development, on the analogy of the Universal Declaration of Human Rights.

No comment (J. Krempelsauer)

Declaration of the Right to Nature Conservation, Environmental Protection and Sustainable Development*

I. General Principles, Rights and Responsibilities

Fundamental Human Rights

1. All human beings have the fundamental right to an environment adequate for their health and well-being.

Inter-Generational Equity

2. States shall conserve and use the environment and natural resources for the benefit of present and future generations.

Conservation and Sustainable Use

3. States shall maintain ecosystems and ecological processes essential for the functioning of the biosphere, shall preserve biological diversity, and shall observe the principle of optimum sustainable yield in the use of living resources and ecosystems.

Environmental Standards and Monitoring

4. States shall establish adequate environmental protection standards and monitor changes in and publish relevant data on environmental quality and resource use.

Prior Environmental Assessments

5. States shall make or require prior environmental assessments of proposed activities which may significantly affect the environment or use of a natural resource.

Prior Notification, Access, and Due Process

6. States shall inform in a timely manner all persons likely to be significantly affected by a planned activity

➡

and grant them equal access and due process in administrative and judicial proceedings.

Sustainable Development and Assistance

7. States shall ensure that conservation is treated as an integral part of the planning and implementation of development activities and provide assistance to other States, especially to developing countries, in support of environmental protection and sustainable development.

General Obligation to Co-operate

8. States shall co-operate in good faith with other States in implementing the preceding rights and obligations.

II. Principles, Rights and Obligations concerning Transboundary Natural Resources and Environmental Interferences

Reasonable and Equitable Use

9. States shall use transboundary natural resources in a reasonable and equitable manner.

Prevention and Abatement

10. States shall prevent or abate any transboundary environmental interference which could cause or causes significant harm (but subject to certain exceptions provided for in Art. 11 and Art. 12 below).

Strict Liability

11. States shall take all reasonable precautionary measures to limit the risk when carrying out or permitting certain dangerous but beneficial activities and shall ensure that compensation is provided should

⇨ substantial transboundary harm occur even when the activities were not known to be harmful at the time they were undertaken.

Prior Agreements When Prevention Costs Greatly Exceed Harm

12. States shall enter into negotiations with the affected State on the equitable conditions under which the activity could be carried out when planning to carry out or permit activities causing transboundary harm which is substantial but far less than the cost of prevention. (If no agreement can be reached, see Art. 22.)

Non-Discrimination

13. States shall apply as a minimum at least the same standards for environmental conduct and impacts regarding transboundary natural resources and environmental interferences as are applied domestically (i.e. do not do to others what you would not do to your own citizens).

General Obligation to Co-operate on Transboundary Environmental Problems

14. States shall co-operate in good faith with other States to achieve optimal use of transboundary natural resources and effective prevention or abatement of transboundary environmental interferences.

Exchange of Information

15. States of origin shall provide timely and relevant information to the other concerned States regarding transboundary natural resources or environmental interferences.

Prior Assessment and Notification

16. States shall provide prior and timely notification and

➡

relevant information to the other concerned States and
shall make or require an environmental assessment of
planned activities which may have significant
transboundary effects.

Prior Consultations

17. States of origin shall consult at an early stage and in
good faith with other concerned States regarding
existing or potential transboundary interferences with
their use of a natural resource or the environment.

Co-operative Arrangements for Environmental Assessment and Protection

18. States shall co-operate with the concerned States in
monitoring, scientific research and standard setting
regarding transboundary natural resources and
environmental interferences.

Emergency Situations

19. States shall develop contingency plans regarding
emergency situations likely to cause transboundary
environmental interferences and shall promptly warn,
provide relevant information to and co-operate with
concerned States when emergencies occur.

Equal Access and Treatment

20. States shall grant equal access, due process and equal
treatment in administrative and judicial proceedings to
all persons who are or may be affected by transboundary
interferences with their use of a natural resource or the
environment.

III. State Responsibility

21. States shall cease activities which breach an
international obligation regarding the environment and
provide compensation for the harm caused.

⇨

IV. Peaceful Settlement of Disputes

22. States shall settle environmental disputes by peaceful means. If mutual agreement on a solution or on other dispute settlement arrangements is not reached within 18 months, the dispute shall be submitted to conciliation and, if unresolved, thereafter to arbitration or judicial settlement at the request of any of the concerned States.

* This summary is based on the more detailed legal formulation in the report to the Brundtland Commission by the international legal experts group. It highlights only the main thrust of the principles and articles. The above text is included in the Brundtland Report as a draft and therefore does not form a proposal by the Commission itself.   ■

The Financial Consequences

The measures needed to protect the global environment will require enormous sums of money. In the past ten years it has been shown that capital expenditure directed at pollution control is a good investment. Any capital invested in a sustainable future is a good investment. We can no longer squander what belongs to our children and grandchildren. We shall have to pay for it. This will be painful, no matter how we go about it.

In the current economic system, the polluter often does not have to pay. According to the Brundtland Commission, environmental costs should be included in all product prices, so that environmentally benign products become cheaper than others.

International measures often need to be financed internationally. In this respect the Brundtland Commission points to the role of international banks as financiers. In this context the World Bank fulfils a key role, for it provides the majority of loans to developing countries and often exerts a substantial influence on their policies. The Brundtland Commission points out that the World Bank has modified its policy and is now more sensitive to environmental problems and sustainable development. Regional Development Banks and the International Monetary Fund must, in the Commission's view, include similar objectives in their policies and programmes.

However, this will not yield enough money for all the measures needed. Creativity should be employed in finding new sources of revenue. Perhaps money can be obtained by levying taxes on the use of

No comment (J. Krempelsauer)

the commons (for instance, the oceans and space). Taxes on scarce goods, such as energy and fossil fuels, would also encourage energy conservation and more economical use of the Earth's resources. Perhaps taxes could even be levied on international trade.

Reactions and Criticisms

Environmental, Third World and peace organizations have criticized the Brundtland Commission, and much of their criticism is incorporated in the preceding chapters. Constructive criticism came from major organizations such as the World Wildlife Fund and the Environmental Liaison Centre. Environmental, Third World and peace organizations have also published reactions on a national level. Sustainable development, the threats to the Earth and possible countermeasures are now prominent items on the agendas of governments, financiers and industry. This represents a major step forward. And many feel that essential changes are in the making. The changes in the policy of the World Bank, which has hired a team of environmental experts to screen its projects for their environmental impact, have been brought about by prolonged pressure of environmental and Third World organizations. This gives hope.

Not everyone is as optimistic, however. Critics assert that there are problems, quite rightly analysed by the Brundtland Commission, which are caused by the Commission's very objectives: economic growth and modernization. These form the starting point of the Report, and no doubts are expressed as to their correctness. The instruments the Commission proposes as solutions have in many cases been the very causes of environmental destruction. Anupam Mishra, an environmentalist in India, says:

> We should not assume that we can look for solutions to our problems within the framework of the current development pattern. It would be folly to think the Brundtland Commission can find solutions within the 'counter-productive framework' of governments, the United Nations, the World Bank and so on. Because the present structures have given us the disease, is it then logical that they should also provide the cure? This seems to be the limitation of this Commission, because it itself stemmed from the current framework.

Anupam Mishra formulates a criticism that is increasingly being voiced in the Third World. To many, the world's major financial institutions and governments represent oppression, and the concept of sustainable development as used by them is no more than a thin veneer serving to conceal the bitter pill of exploitation and tyranny. Much, very much, needs to be done before this image changes.

The Role of the World Bank

'We are waking up to the fact that if Africa is dying it is because her environment has been plundered, overexploited and neglected,' Mrs. Raheb W. Mwatha told the Brundtland Commission at a public hearing in September 1986. Edward Goldsmith, editor of *The Ecologist*, one of the oldest and most esteemed environmental magazines, in an open letter to the President of the World Bank, states the case thus:

> You must know this, Mr. Conable. Your Bank's role in plundering, overexploiting and neglecting the environment of the Third World has been pointed out to you in innumerable well-written and highly documented studies by such writers as Susan George, Joe Collins and Frances Moore Lappé, Teresa Hayter, Catherine Watson and Cheryl Payer, to name but a few, and also by environmental organizations such as the Environmental Defense Fund (EDF), The Sierra Club, Survival International, Friends of the Earth (FOE), not to mention ourselves here.
>
> It has even been pointed out to you on many occasions by members of your own staff. Indeed yours is the only multilateral development bank to have its own environmental department. What is more, it employs several highly competent ecologists. But you have invariably chosen to ignore their warnings and regard environmental considerations as little more than impediments to the achievement of your real priorities.

The Fatal Five

In an article in the Dutch magazine *Natuur en Milieu* (April 1987), Wouter Veening of the international nature conservation organization, IUCN, said the following about 'the disastrous banking practices of the World Bank':

➡

⇨

The most infamous World Bank project is the Palonoroeste project that is to open up the Brazilian state of Rondonia in the Amazon region. The World Bank is financing road construction in virgin tropical forests, which in 1980 still covered virtually all of the state. The roads open up Rondonia to extremely poor, landless farmers from South Brazil, to adventurers and to land speculators. The Indians and rubber tappers, now living in harmony with the forest without harming it, are being expelled from their home grounds — they are often in fact chased away at gunpoint — and the farmers move in. (. . .) What remains is a ghostly landscape, with half-burnt trees and stagnant pools, which are major sources of malaria. The farmers soon have no other option but to move on. In a few years' time the entire state of Rondonia, an area as big as West Germany, will be bare. Already, not enough land is available for the continuing inflow of immigrants. For this reason, the Inter-American Development Bank, a regional sister of the World Bank, recently undertook to finance roads that are to open up the neighbouring state of Acre, even deeper in the Amazon region.

This development project in Brazil is one of the 'fatal five' in which the World Bank is involved. Other projects in this fatal five, which environmental organizations have made priorities in their campaign against World Bank policy, are the planned Three Gorges Dam on the Yangtse River in China, which will flood thousands of square kilometres and force three million people to move; large-scale cattle ranching projects in Botswana, which will cause overgrazing of vulnerable local ecosystems; the destructive dam and irrigation projects in the Narmada Valley of India; and the transmigration project in Indonesia, which calls for more or less forced emigration of millions of people (often a total failure) to unspoiled areas on other islands in the archipelago.

Objections

The World Bank is one of the major international

➡

⇨ policy-making institutions. Many countries consider the
World Bank the think tank for development co-
operation. So far, the environment has not played any
significant role in its policy, though back in 1970 a
representative of the Bank, Ernesto Franco, stated that
'the Bank is taking steps to ensure that the projects it
finances do not have significant adverse ecological
consequences.'

The most fundamental criticism is that the World Bank
has opened up the Third World to international private
enterprise, disregarding the social, cultural, economic
and ecological interests of the countries and their
inhabitants. While making huge profits, private
corporations provide the consumer societies in the rich
North and the elites in the poor South with the goods
they have been taught to crave for. Whether directly or
indirectly, major forms of exploitation are supported by
World Bank loans. World Bank thinking is elitist and
Western-oriented. Profit, and production for those who
have the capital and the power, are its central precepts.
Its ultimate goal is modernization and Westernization of
the world for the benefit of the elites it serves.

Similar criticisms apply to most of the other financial
institutions, such as the International Monetary Fund
(IMF), which in its debt negotiations forces poor
countries to sell out. In Wouter Veening's words: 'Thus,
under pressure from the International Monetary Fund,
health care, education and food subsidies have to bleed
in order to promote exports of, for instance, tobacco.'

Changes

The World Bank is not insensitive to external pressure. All
major public institutions find it very important to keep up
a certain image. In this respect, the ecological crisis does
affect the World Bank. This could be the reason
underlying its President's announcement, in 1987, that the
World Bank will adopt a new policy with respect to the
ecological consequences of its projects. In the future, ➡

⇨

environmental impact assessments will form an integral part of all major projects, and the Bank's environmental staff will be greatly expanded. This policy shift has been welcomed with cautious enthusiasm by the environmental movement. A change in policy could have profound effects, for large sums of money are involved. In addition, the environmentalists say, we really have no choice. Banks are here to stay; this is something we cannot change. All we can do is try and change the policies of the big moneylenders. But are the banks serious when they promise to change their policies, or are they merely trying to get rid of their hard, ruthless image? There are very real reasons for doubt.

Catherine Watson, a former employee of the World Bank's environmental department, concluded that: 'If our proposals were accepted, it was because they enhanced the Bank's progressive image while costing little. Proposals that threatened the future of a project or that had major consequences for the work of the Bank were rejected as being unrealistic and impracticable.'

The President of the World Bank, Mr. Conable, elicited furious reactions last year by stating that 'the World Bank is the largest single source of financing and preservation of the tropical forest' and that 'these past ten years the investments and technical support by the World Bank in the field of forestry have exceeded one billion dollars.' These investments were made mostly in projects that destroyed forests. The World Bank is still supporting the Fatal Five projects.

Open Letter

In his open letter to the President of the World Bank, Edward Goldsmith goes to the heart of the matter:

> Such projects only satisfy the short-term financial and political interests of a small group of bankers, bureaucrats, industrialists, engineers and politicians. (. . .) The short-term interests of such a group are totally incompatible with

➡

⇨

the long-term interests and needs of an increasingly impoverished humanity. You told the World Resources Institute in May 1987 of new policies and new concern for the environment. Will you now signify your genuine concern by immediate cancellation of financial aid for indefensible projects such as the Narmada and Bodhghat Dams and the Great Carajas Project* and at the same time reappraise all other World Bank projects, using a yardstick which measures the needs of humanity, our children and the biosphere, on whose preservation life itself must ultimately depend? Only then will you be able to persuade the world that your new concern for the environment is a genuine one.

* Narmada and Bodhghat are in India, Great Carajas in Brazil.

7. Recent Developments

Our Common Future had appeared, since it was launched in April 1987, in 17 languages by September 1989 and has generated scores of other publications commenting on and developing aspects of its policy recommendations, as well as extensive TV, radio and other media coverage. A Centre for *Our Common Future* has been created in Geneva as a focal point for the environmental activities of governments, multilateral institutions, scientific bodies, industry as well as non-governmental organizations.

The United Nations System

UN agencies are redirecting their activities towards meeting the priorities the Report lays down for them. The United Nations Development Programme (UNDP), for example, reported that it is expanding its scientific and managerial capacity for providing technical co-operation and pre-investment support in the area of environment. The World Bank is expanding its collaboration with NGOs on the ground, particularly in Third World countries, and is putting into effect a new grant programme aimed at accelerating the preparation of innovative environmental projects. It seems that all UN organizations want to say something on the issue. None of the reactions, however, have been particularly revolutionary in content. The International Atomic Energy Agency (IAEA), for instance, actually had the temerity to state that 'the supply of energy for economic growth in a sustainable and environmentally acceptable manner is a central activity in the Agency's programme.' Environmental groups have heard this before. Also, activities of the World Bank and other UN agencies are being watched with considerable scepticism. How much is just talk, how much is real change?

The United Nations 1992 Global Conference on Environment and

Development is in preparation. It will mark the 20th anniversary of the Stockholm Conference which first put the environment on the world agenda. Set to coincide with World Environment Day, June 5th 1992, the two-week conference will bring together governments 'at the highest level of participation' and all relevant international institutions, the scientific community, industry, trade unions and non-governmental organizations. The aim will be to find ways of promoting sustainable and environmentally sound development in all countries and to seek 'preventive measures at the sources of environmental and natural resources degradation'.

Governments

By March 1989, two years after the publication of the Brundtland Report, 22 countries and the European Community had responded with details of their progress towards the achievement of sustainable development policies. In many other countries reports are still being prepared. The impact of Brundtland has certainly been high-level discussions within many governments placing environment nearer the top of their political agenda. Many governments have organized major meetings, often involving scientific organizations and NGOs. In Spring 1990 in Bergen the Economic Commission of Europe is holding a high-level meeting with the title 'Action for a Common Future', to review progress made so far on issues highlighted by the Brundtland Report.

Non-governmental Organizations

Of the countless local, national and international NGOs which have made themselves custodians of the 'Our Common Future' ideal, so many have made outstanding contributions that it becomes harder all the time to keep abreast of their efforts. All over the world, NGOs have written position papers, put together coalitions to propagate the Brundtland ideas locally, and have tried to influence policies by publicizing their responses to the Report. Indeed it is possible to spend almost all one's time attending meetings, organized by NGOs as follow-ups to the Brundtland Report. And these meetings do not cause smoke and dust. Groups get together for concrete action. Development agencies and charities are realizing that they have not thought deeply enough about environmental concerns. Peace groups are linking up with environmental groups. The coalitions that result are strong enough to get at least a part of their demands recognized by the politicians. In addition, associated with the many meetings of powerful national and multilateral bodies like the World Bank, NGOs are creating coalitions to lobby for a more vigorous implementation of their demands.

The Media

It is not difficult now, at least in the West, for individuals and organizations to find the right video, film, article, tape or other material needed to inform the audiences they wish to reach. Excellent TV productions, including the outstanding 15 minute 'Our Common Future' video, have been distributed. The London-based Television Trust for the Environment (TVE) is now operating a subsidized 'Moving Pictures' distribution service, sending high-quality TV programmes on environment and development to developing countries and NGOs.

International Financial Institutions

The Report's recommendations that multilateral financial institutions should do more to help countries develop long-term strategies for sustainable development seems to be finding an echo on many levels. The Asian Development Bank claims to have translated the Report's recommendations into action with regional technical assistance grants totalling $1,340 million. Other banks, like the World Bank and the Inter-American Development Bank have expressed concern on the issue. But it has to be said that the financial institutions do not yet seem to have made real changes in the direction of sustainable development.

Industry

The environment is fast becoming a popular, new public relations tool for the private sector. Australia's mining industry, in line with its government, now conducts public information programmes on the environment, supports the environmental sciences financially and touts its own environmental management expertise to the community. Alcoa of Australia Ltd., a major aluminium producer, has indeed extensive experience in land reclamation and forestry, and is now making this expertise available to outside organizations through its Tree Technology Project. Other giants, also, are active. IBM UK has published a brochure *Searching for Survival*. Imperial Chemical Industries, one of the most notorious polluters in Britain, has produced a booklet entitled: *Industry and the Environment: A Question of Balance*.

Making up the Balance

It is not yet possible to say really what the Brundtland Report did or did not achieve. It came at a time of crisis, a time when such a report could fill a gap felt by many people and institutions.

So far, little concrete has been achieved despite all the meetings, and the hype and publicity accompanying them. On the other hand, from the viewpoint of a grassroots activist, changes can be distinguished. Movements are getting together and sharing resources. There is much more money available to undertake research. And non-governmental organizations working on environment and development in the South are experiencing a positive response in Northern funding circles. Even at governmental level, one can see some changes. Ministries are working on integrated environment and development plans. Environment and Development, as a topic which needs attention and which can only be understood in its mutual interrelationship, is being recognized. The Brundtland Report has certainly helped in creating this recognition.

Address of the Centre for Our Common Future
Palais Wilson, 52 Rue des Pâquis, CH – 1201 Geneva, Switzerland.
Tel. (022) 7327117
Tlx. 27910 CH
Fax. (022) 7385046

8. Sustainable Development: Some Concluding Reflections

Development means change. And most people want a change for the better. The aims of development, of course, should depend on our particular ethics, culture and religion. But the dominant pattern of development today is based on Western culture which has created a universal order: universal values, universal economics, universal science. 'This concept of universalism has its foundations in the political creed and philosophy of European liberal thought which proclaimed the ushering in of the industrial mode of production. The political philosophers emphasized the importance of private endeavour, private interests, private profits: competition and utilitarianism were its cornerstones.'[1] Other cultures, in contrast, have very different concepts of development, and therefore different aims and processes.

But we all share a similar concern. The current mode of development cannot sustain itself. The destruction of our environment, increasing poverty and injustice, the finite nature of our resources show that a drastic change in our pattern of development is needed. The 'non-sustainability' of our global society is evident. But the unjust and violent structure of our society is also becoming more and more visible.

Different Paradigms

In *The Ecologist* (Vol. 19, No. 3, 1989), two of India's leading scientists and environmental activists, Vandana Shiva and Jayanta Bandyo-padhyay, argued that:

> The ideology of the dominant pattern of development derives its driving force from a linear theory of progress, from a vision of historical evolution created in eighteenth and nineteenth century Western Europe and universalized throughout the world, especially in the post-war development

decades. The linearity of history, pre-supposed in this theory of progress, created an ideology of development that equated development with economic growth, economic growth with expansion of the market economy, modernity with consumerism, and non-market economics with backwardness. The diverse traditions of the world, with their distinctive technological, ecological, economic, political and cultural structures, were driven by this new ideology to converge into a homogeneous monolithic order modelled on the particular evolution of the West.

According to these writers, and many other representatives of non-governmental organizations, it is the concept of economic growth which is the cause of our crisis: 'Economic growth was a new colonialism, draining resources away from those who needed them most. The discontinuity lay in the fact that it was now new national elites, not colonial powers, that masterminded the exploitation on grounds of "national interest" and growing gross national products, and it was accomplished with more powerful technologies of appropriation and destruction.'[2]

The dominant development paradigm disregarded the complexity of all processes on Earth, often strongly related to each other. The most pronounced example of an approach which stresses the inter-relatedness of all things, is the Gaia Hypothesis. Jim Lovelock, one of the leading proponents of this theory, describes the world as one organism. For Lovelock, 'the entire range of living matter on Earth, from whales to viruses, and from oaks to algae, could be regarded as a single living entity, capable of manipulating the Earth's atmosphere to suit its overall needs.' This organism, of which human society is a part, but only one part, regulates her activities in a very complex and subtle way. For such a world, terms such as 'order', 'teleology', 'integrity', 'co-operation', 'stability' and 'internalized control' are the keys. The Gaia concept relates to what is known in ecology as a climax situation (see below).

The opposite to this concept is an approach which sees the planet Earth, with her natural resources, merely as a space to be used by the people who live on it. The aim of development is, therefore, to cream off the best of available resources in order to exchange them for money on the world market. This approach aims at the maximization of production. Comparing it with the Gaia Hypothesis, one could say that this ideology of capital accumulation in the world market aims at a world which is constantly in a pioneer situation (in contrast to the climax situation). It is very productive, but with very little diversity and little internal self-control. This system values competition higher than co-operation. The individual is more important than the community. And external factors dominate the system which is inherently unstable.

Pioneer World View versus a Climax World View

Edward Goldsmith, editor of *The Ecologist*, explains the difference between a pioneer and a climax situation as follows:[3]

> A pioneer ecosystem, that is to say an ecosystem in the earliest stages of development, or one that has been ravaged by some discontinuity such as a volcanic eruption or an industrial development scheme, displays a whole constellation of closely related features. In a sense, such an ecosystem is the least 'living' of ecosystems or, more precisely, the one in which the basic features of living things are least apparent, for the obvious reason that they have not yet had time to develop. Such an ecosystem is among other things highly productive, which of course endears it to our modern production-oriented society which can cream off the apparently surplus biomass, process it, and put it up for sale on the international market. The reason why it is so highly productive, of course, is because as soon as it is brought into being, so the healing processes of nature are brought into operation and the ecosystem changes rapidly via the different stages of ecological succession until it achieves that state which resembles, as closely as possible, the original climax.
>
> The climax or adult ecosystem, on the other hand, is very unproductive. This must be so both because the climax is the most stable state possible in the local biotic, abiotic and climatic circumstances, and because the achievement of such a stable state appears to be the basic goal of living things. Once achieved, change is kept to a minimum.

The productivity of a pioneer system depends largely on external inputs. During an initial period of rapid production the system becomes exhausted. In order to keep production high in a monoculture system one needs to invest in fertilizers, irrigation and pesticides. In the long run, taking into account the costs of those inputs (economic, environmental and social costs), total production will be relatively low. The Green Revolution in Punjab shows that after ten to twenty years of intensive agriculture, the productivity of the land drops to a level which makes it impossible to sustain its population. Inputs, in the sense of fertilizers, pesticides and irrigation, demand enormous investments, so high indeed that it is impossible to prevent a dramatic drop in production levels. One result in Punjab is that these farmers who are capable of doing so, flee the country to set up a new farm or end up in a miserable state as environmental refugees in the ever increasing slums of the cities. A tropical rain forest, mangrove forest or coral reef — typical climax systems — could very well supply a higher level of production, taking into account that, in the long run, no large external inputs are needed and the system can maintain itself by preventing losses to the outside. This production cannot be expressed simply in market values. In a tropical forest, for instance, 'the functions fulfilled by non-timber forest products in the rural household economy include providing: food security in the form of staples, or, more frequently, nutritional supplements, such as snacks and side-dishes, and buffers against seasonal and emergency shortages; health care in the form of ingredients in the traditional medicines (for which substitutes may not be available or affordable); raw materials for building, and implements for household use or for use in support of other economic activities — agriculture, fishing, hunting or small-scale processing and manufacturing enterprises; and, finally, income and employment from the collection, trade or processing and manufacture of non-timber products.'[4]

One should not confuse the terms 'change' and 'dynamics'. A climax situation can entail a lot of internal dynamics. Think of a tropical rain forest in which the changes within the ecosystem can take place extremely rapidly. A tree dies, is consumed by fungi, insects and other organisms, and within a short period nothing of the tree is left. But nothing is lost either. In an extremely efficient and rapid way the whole biomass has been turned into a new tissue. The cycles are closed.

The Gaia Hypothesis, in contrast to the Western development model, sees the Earth as a climax or adult ecosystem, which is by no means either as productive or as invulnerable to disruption as we have been brought up to believe.

Women

Yet another perspective needs to be taken into account when we think about development, as Corinne Kumar-D'souza from India explains:

Science and its world view may, through its laws, explain the appearance, even the structure of phenomena, using its tools of quantification and objectification, but does not, and cannot, capture their essence. It reduces the history of whole people into frames of progress, to lines of poverty, to models of development: it writes the history of whole epochs, leaving out the women who are half of human experience, and in so doing can never penetrate the depths of the different rhythms of cultures, never grasp the meaning of the different idioms of civilizations, never understand the different cosmologies of the women, the *daliths*,the blacks, never discover the knowledges of those who are on the margins, the edges.[5]

There is a clear link between the dominant paradigm of development and the domination of males in this world. In his *De Dignitate et Augmentis Scientiarum* (1623), the European philosopher and scientist, Bacon, makes this very clear when he states that the scientist should subject nature to his needs, make *her* a slave, and give *her* form through mechanical techniques — the reason being that that is how one can find out *her* 'intrigues' and 'secrets'.[6] As Western culture has come to dominate the whole world, the consequences of this approach have become more and more clear.

Susan Griffin, in her remarkable book *Woman and Nature*,[7] describes these consequences in her chapter on Land — and it is worth quoting at length:

He breaks the wilderness. He clears the land of trees, bush, weed. The land is brought under his control; he has turned waste into a garden. Into her soil he places his plow. He labors. He plants. He sows. By the sweat of his brow, he makes her yield. She opens her broad lap to him. She smiles on him. She prepares him a feast. She gives up her treasures to him. She makes him grow rich. She yields. She conceives. Her lap is fertile. Out of her dark interior, life arises. What she does to his seed is a mystery to him. He counts her yielding as a miracle. He sees her working as effortless. Whatever she brings forth he calls his own. He has made her conceive. His land is a mother. She smiles on the joys of her children. She feeds him generously. Again and again, in his hunger, he returns to her. Again and again she gives to him. She is his mother. Her powers are a mystery to him. Silently she works miracles for him. Yet, just as silently, she withholds from him. Without reason, she refuses to yield. She is fickle. She dries up. She is bitter. She scorns him. He is determined he will master her. He will make her produce at will. He will devise ways to plant what he wants in her, to make her yield more to him.

He deciphers the secrets of the soil. (He knows why she brings forth.) He recites the story of the carbon cycle. (He masters the properties of chlorophyll.) He recites the story of the nitrogen cycle. (He brings nitrogen out of the air.) He determines the composition of the soil. (Over and over he can plant the same plot of land with the same crop.) He says that the soil is a lifeless place of storage, he says that the soil is what is tilled by farmers. He says that the land need no longer lie fallow. That what went on in her quietude is no longer a secret, that the ways of the land can be managed. That the farmer can ask whatever he wishes of the land. (He replaces the fungi, bacteria, earthworms, insects, decay.) He names all that is necessary, nitrogen, phosphorus, potassium, and these he says he can make. He increases the weight of kernels of barley with potash; he makes a more mealy potato with muriate of potash; he makes the color of cabbage bright green with nitrate; he makes onions which live longer with phosphates; he makes the cauliflower head early by withholding nitrogen.

His powers continue to grow. Phosphoric acid, nitrogen fertilizers, ammonium sulphate, white phosphate, potash, iron sulphate, nitrate of soda, superphosphate, calcium cynanamide, calcium oxide, calcium magnesium, zinc sulphate, phenobarbital, amphetamine, magnesium, oestrogen, copper sulphate, meprobamate, thalidomide, benzethonium chloride, Valium, hexachlorophene, diethylstilbestrol.

What devices she can use to continue she does. She says that the pain is unbearable. Give me something, she says. What he gives her she takes into herself without asking why. She says now that the edges of what she sees are blurred. The edges of what she sees, and what she wants, and what she is saying, are blurred. Give me something, she says. What he gives her she takes without asking. She says that the first pain is gone, or that she cannot remember it, or that she cannot remember why this began, or what she was like before, or if she will survive without what he gives her to take, but that she does not know, or cannot remember, why she continues.

He says she cannot continue without him. He says she must have what he gives her. He says also that he protects her from predators. That he gives her dichlorodiphenyltrichloroethane, dieldrin, chlorinated naphthalenes, chlordan, parathion, Malathion, selenium, pentachlorophenol, arsenic, sodium arsenite, amitrole. That he has rid her of pests, he says.

And he had devised ways to separate himself from her. He sends machines to do his labor. His working has become as effortless as hers. He accomplishes days of labor with a small motion of his hand. His efforts are more astonishing than hers. No longer praying, no longer imploring, he pronounces words from a distance and his orders are carried out. Even with his back turned to her she yields to him. And in his mind, he imagines that he can conceive without her. In his mind he develops the means to supplant her miracles with his own. In his mind, he no longer relies on her. What he possesses, he says, is his to use and to abandon.

The 'issue' of women and development has been dealt with in the dominant institutions of our world. There is hardly any development organization or multilateral bank or even development consultancy without a 'women's desk'. But it becomes clear from Bacon's remarks as one of the main founders of modern science, and the description of Susan Griffin, quoted above, the 'issue' has in fact nothing to do with extending the outreach of development aid to women as an essential 'target-group'. As Vandana Shiva put it: 'By the end of the UN Decade for Women, it was becoming clear that development itself was the problem. Insufficient and inadequate "participation" in "Development" was not the cause for women's increasing underdevelopment: it was, rather, their enforced but asymmetric participation in it, by which they bore the costs but were excluded from the benefits, that was responsible for their marginalization.'[8] To quote Corinne Kumar-D'souza again:

> Most women in the Third World are poor women. Most refugees are women. Millions of women are sought to be 'integrated' and brought into the mainstream of its processes of economic modernization. Women, we are told, are to be added: their numbers increased; their share in resources, land, income, improved. This will assure the development of women. Never mind that these structures are euro-centric, andro-centric. The Third World is being 'integrated' into the existing unequal and exploitive structures of development. Should we seek a similar integration? Shall we learn the female-prone skills of sewing, knitting, embroidery and participate in the income-generating projects? Shall we attend the women's literacy classes and learn to accept our prescribed role and status in society? Should we be thankful to the technologists (the appropriate ones, no doubt) for making 'our' burden easier and inventing the gobar gas plants, the smokeless chulas and grinders? Shall we assimilate ourselves into a process over which we have no control; merge into a model, the terms of which have been defined for us?[9]

Critique of the Dominant Culture

The dominant society creates images and ideologies which translate perceptions of the world into fears and hopes. These ideologies and images are deeply rooted in many of us. Discussions on sustainable development often end up in discussions on our ability to 'control ourselves'. 'People destroy their environment.' 'The problem is that there are too many people.' 'The only thing we can hope for is a big disaster which will teach us to change.' This is the way such discussions often end.

Or to quote Susan Griffin again:

> 'All organic beings are exposed to severe competition,' it is written. And it is observed that all creatures are pressed into a struggle for existence.
> That all plants of a given country are at war with one another.
> That it is the tendency of all beings to multiply faster than their source of nourishment.
> (Indeed, it is written that the human race tends to outrun subsistence and is kept in bounds only by famine, pestilence or war.)
> And this struggle is called a natural government, and this warfare is said to lead to perfection.

(And it is suggested that war serves 'for the real health of humanity and the building of strong races.')
(And it is declared that the history of human society is the history of class struggle. That the collisions between the classes will end in the victory of the proletariat.)
(And the development of large corporations, it is pointed out, is also merely the survival of the fittest, merely the working out of a law of nature and a law of God.)[10]

Critiquing these 'images' means critiquing the dominant conception of development. The critiques from the women quoted here and from the people supporting the Gaia Hypothesis converge in a concept of a development which is based on restoring internal control, creating stability and peaceful co-operation. Such a concept doesn't allow strong external influences. It will maximize 'stocks' (physical, intellectual, ecological) and will minimize the movement and export of things (in the form of goods, natural resources, capital and so on). Essentially, it runs contrary to the open market system. Sustainable development in this sense will demand solving the problem of domination in society elites (and therefore also by men). It is in this sense also a critique and action against the dominant paradigm of development. Sustainable development (if one wishes to use the term) therefore means solving a conflict which is rooted deep in our images of the world and the organization of our society.

The Report of the World Commission on Environment and Development does not contain any of this critique. Its authors are part of the elite which is being criticized. The Brundtland Commission chose to point at poverty itself as main cause of environmental disruption and could not identify its own position in this context. It is therefore logical that the dominant powers in the world embraced the Report as one of the most progressive and important of the decade.

The Six Principles of Sustainable Development

Based on discussions going on in environmental, development and peace groups, it is possible to describe six general principles[11] which can help us to understand what kind of development we want. The principles are general, as they should be, but also basic to a development process we want and need. The principles define an ideal state and since we start from a conflict, often in the worst condition, the process of achieving the principles is as important as the principles themselves.

(1) The principle of the cultural and social integrity of development: Quoting a statement from Lloyd Timberlake, it would mean that 'development must grow from within, and not be slapped on from the outside'.

(2) The ecological principle: Development must be compatible with and restore diversity and rely on sustainable forms of resource use.

(3) The solidarity principle: Development must provide the basic necessities of life and secure living conditions for *all* people, promote equity, and avoid unequal exchange.

(4) The emancipation principle: Development must foster self-reliance, local control over resources, empowerment and participation by the underprivileged and marginalized, and opportunities for action people can feel is fulfilling.

(5) The non-violence principle: Development must be peaceful, both in the direct sense (the non-use of physical violence) and in the structural sense (violence as embodied in the institutions of society).

(6) The principle of error friendliness: Development must allow for mistakes without endangering the integrity of the immediate ecosystem and resource base.[12]

These six principles as a way of conceiving of sustainable development as a much more root and branch alternative to the present Western model of development than the Brundtland Report was prepared to do in its rather anodyne use of the term, make several things clear. First of all, there is a danger of putting emphasis on ecological considerations to the exclusion of other, equally important and valid considerations. It is tempting to do this at a time when the destruction of our environment is one of the most visible causes of the finity of our civilization. But we should be careful not to forget the strong inter-relatedness of all six principles of the kind of development we need.

Secondly, accepting the fact that the principles rely on each other, we are confronted with the question of how to implement all these principles at one and the same time. We are not starting from a neutral position but from a conflict. The process through which we can reach those six principles in the organization of our societies and economies is therefore a different matter, but of no less concern. Yet little work has been done on describing such a possible process, even if much of the struggle of people in the world has in fact been aimed at preserving societies based on the six principles (think, for a moment, of the many self-sufficient farming communities and indigenous peoples' societies which have been destroyed).

Positive Synergisms[13]

Science has (re)discovered synergisms — the complex interaction of different factors strengthening certain processes in a stronger way than the mere sum of the separate processes would have done. Air pollution is a clear example of a complex and synergistic system. A certain amount of sulphur dioxide will hardly damage trees; nor would ozone do so; or low temperatures combined with fog. But these four elements together could spell death for a forest. For they would interact in a complex way, strengthen each other's influence, thereby weakening fatally the resistance of the trees.

What we need, in contrast, are positive synergisms. Positive synergisms are also extremely complex but that is exactly what we should expect and aim at. There are no simple answers to complex problems.

Consider a few examples of what might be achieved:

- In several countries farming within the boundaries of the cities is being promoted. People are growing vegetables in the slum areas. The impact is enormous. The vegetables demand taking care of the land, hygiene, social control. They mean food, income, and also less dependence on food from the market. They provide insurance in bad times. They bring health since the food is rich in nutrients, and that means less dependence on medicines, more income and less risk (because when you are sick you cannot work, so you have no income). Urban vegetable growing can create a positive spiral in which all the six principles play a role.

- Construction of a community latrine can also change a slum totally. Sulabh International, an Indian organization with its roots in the Gandhian movement, started to construct community latrines in slum areas. They are based on a very simple principle which Gandhi himself promoted all his life. Constructed on waste dumps which had been infested with diseases since there were no latrines in the area, the Sulabh projects have transformed slums like those of Patna in North India. People pay a small amount for the use of the latrine, the money going to pay a person to keep it clean. They receive soap, clean water and the use of a latrine in exchange. Women and beggars are allowed in for free. Thousands of people make use of the service. The hygiene of the area changes rapidly for the better. Much attention has been paid to the surroundings of the latrine. The human waste is converted into fertilizer which in its turn is used to grow food in the slum area, in its turn creating jobs, better health and improved nutrition. A part of the human excreta can be used in biogas plants producing energy which can be used for lighting the streets, so creating a safer place to be. The women, for whom the non-existence of latrines has been a major problem, can also feel safer.

●   Social fencing is a process of change in which a community decides not to use a part of the land in order to restore it. More and more examples of community action in that direction can be found. The process itself is more important than the goals. People organize and share resources. They make themselves dependent on each other, thereby strengthening internal control. They share resources like water and land, since the landless too take part in the scheme. Most social fencing schemes allow for natural reforestation in which the restored areas follow their natural cycle of regeneration towards reconstituting a forest. Many of the original species of trees and animals return. Medicines and other materials, which traditionally came from these forests, can be found again, making the community less dependent on outside trade, thereby creating economic security for many of the villagers.

These are just a few examples of approaches based on positive synergisms. Publications like *Bankrolling Successes* and *The Greening of Aid* refer to many of these kinds of activities.[14] Most of them are not without conflict and often vulnerable to influences from the outside. But they do bear a message of hope. Something can be done. The destruction of our planet is not based on some mythical law of nature but on a conflict, a very human conflict, arising from the domination of some people over other people. But what men and women have done, they can undo or do again differently. Sustainable development — seen as the fundamental recasting of perceptions, values and goals, as embodied in the six principles, holds out a key which we can grasp in our efforts to shape Our Common Future.

Notes

1. 'The South Wind', Corinne Kumar-D'souza, *Sangharsh*, No. 3, 1989.
2. Vandana Shiva, 'Let us survive: women, ecology and development,' Research Foundation for Science and Ecology, Dehradun, *Sangharsh*, No. 3, 1989.
3. Edward Goldsmith, 'Gaia: Some Implications for Theoretical Ecology,' *The Ecologist*, Vol. 18, No. 2., 1988.
4. J. Falconer, 'The major significance of minor forest products: local people's use and values of forest in the West African Humid Forest Zone,' Forestry Department, FAO, Rome (in press), quoted in J. De Beer and McDermott (1989), *The Economic Value of Non-timber Forest Products in Southeast Asia*, Netherlands Committee for IUCN, Amsterdam.
5. 'The South Wind,' op. cit.
6. In Catharina J. M. Halkes '. . . en alles zal worden herschapen'. *Gedachten over de heelwording van de schepping in het spanningsveld tussen natuur en cultuur*, Ten Have/Baarn, 1989.
7. Susan Griffin, *Woman and Nature: The Roaring Inside Her*, The Women's Press, 1984.
8. Vandana Shiva, 'Let us survive,' op. cit.
9. 'The South Wind,' op. cit.
10. Susan Griffin, *Woman and Nature*, op. cit.
11. The principles are described in Florentine Krause, *Energy for Sustainable Development, Part One: The Soft Path Perspective*, IPSEP/ELC, 1985 and Ernst and Christine von Weizsacker, *How to Live With Errors: On the Evolutionary Powers of Errors*, Institute for European Environmental Policy, Bonn, 1986.
12. This is a fairly unknown principle. Ernst and Christine von Weizsacker of the Institute for European Environmental Policy introduced the term. As they explained: 'A society should allow for mistakes as long as they teach you something.' They illustrate the point by referring to how children learn: 'When children learn to walk and to climb, you let them climb on the sofa or on a chair. But not on the window sill of the third floor. Why? Because they are likely to fall, and when they fall from the sofa, it hurts but they can try again. A drop of 8 metres, however, is likely to put a stop to all further exploration.' One can also see the 'scale of development' in this light. The smaller the scale, the higher the error friendliness. The scale should fit the errors (and the efficiency demanded) one can make.
13. Positive synergism is a term used by Nigel Harle of Borderland Archives (Cortenbachstraat 32, 6136 CH Sittard, Netherlands) in several of his articles.
14. Czech Conroy and Miles Litvinoff, *The Greening of Aid, Sustainable Livelihoods in Practice*, 1988, Earthscan Publications Ltd in association with the International Institute for Environment and Development, London.